M000107818

SCIENCE FUSION

Assessment Guide

Grade 1

HOUGHTON MIFFLIN HARCOURT

Acknowledgments for Cover Photos

Front Cover: *lion cub* ©Cesar Lucas Abreu/Stone/Getty Images; *grass background* ©Nicholas Eveleigh/Stockbyte/Getty Images; *field of tulips* ©John McAnulty/Corbis; *soccer players* ©Jon Feingersh Photography Inc/Blend Images/Getty Images; *volcano* ©Westend61 GmbH/Alamy; *microscope* ©Thom Lang/Corbis.

Printed in the U.S.A.

ISBN 978-0-547-59311-1

14 0982 16
4500608321 C D E F G

Contents

Unit 3 Animals

Unit 4 Plants

Unit 5 Environments

Unit 6 Earth's Resources

Unit 7 Weather and Seasons

Unit 8 Objects in the Sky

Unit 9 All About Matter

Unit 10 Forces and Energy

Cumulative Tests

Overview

ScienceFusion provides parallel instructional paths for meeting the content and inquiry objectives in each unit. You may choose to use the print path, digital path, or a combination of both. The quizzes, tests, and other resources in this Assessment Guide may be used with any path you choose.

The *ScienceFusion* assessment options are intended to give you maximum flexibility in assessing what your students know and can do. The program's formative, summative, and performance assessment categories reflect the understanding that assessment is a learning opportunity for students and that all students must demonstrate standards mastery at the end of a school year.

Formative Assessment

At the end of each lesson in the Student Edition, the Brain Check will help you evaluate how well students grasped the concepts taught. The opportunities for students to annotate their Student Edition, including the Active Reading features, can also provide insight into how well students are learning the concepts.

Opportunities are provided throughout the program for students to check their progress and understanding. At the end of each unit, a student self-assessment prompts students to return to areas in which they may need additional work.

The Teacher Edition offers a number of additional tools for formative assessment. Look for the science note-booking strategies Generate Ideas and Summarize Ideas that begin and end many of the two-page sections of the lessons. These strategies provide numerous ways to informally assess whether students are remembering what they read and getting the main ideas. Questions that address a variety of dimensions—including concept development, inquiry skills, and use of reading strategies—are strategically placed throughout each lesson. Located in this Assessment Guide is yet another tool, the Observation Checklist, on which you can record observations of students' ability to use science inquiry skills.

Summative Assessment

To help you reinforce and assess mastery of unit objectives, *ScienceFusion* includes both reviews and tests. You will find the Unit Reviews in the Student Edition. Lesson Quizzes and Unit Tests are provided in this Assessment Guide. All of these assessment tools include multiple-choice formats that mirror standardized statewide assessment formats. Unit Tests also contain short-response and extended-response items. Also included in this Assessment Guide are three Cumulative Tests that cover all the standards of the program.

Performance Assessment

Performance tasks provide evidence of students' ability to use science inquiry skills and critical thinking to complete an authentic task. A brief performance task is included in the Teacher Edition with each Unit Review. A more comprehensive performance task is provided for each unit in this Assessment Guide. Each includes teacher directions and a scoring rubric.

Self-Assessment and Portfolio Assessment

Students should be challenged to reflect on their work and monitor their learning. Several checklists are provided for this purpose. Self-Assessment—Active Reading, Experiment/Project Summary Sheet, Self-Assessment—My Science Notebook, Science Experiences Record, and Guide to My Science Portfolio can be used by students to describe or evaluate their own experiences and projects. Opportunities for self-assessment and evaluation are embedded at key points on the digital path.

Online Assessment

All of the quizzes and tests within this Assessment Guide are available in computer-scored format with the *ScienceFusion* online resources. Banks of items from which tests can be built are also available.

Test-Taking Tips

Understandably, students often experience test-related anxiety. Teaching students to apply a number of general test-taking strategies may bolster their confidence and result in improved student performance on formal assessment. As students take a test, they should

- scan the entire test first before answering any questions.
- read the directions slowly and carefully before beginning a section.
- begin with the easiest questions or most familiar material.
- read the question and all answer options before selecting an answer.
- watch out for key words such as *not, least, best, most,* and so on.
- carefully analyze graphs, tables, diagrams, and pictures that accompany items.
- double-check answers to catch and correct errors.
- erase all mistakes completely and write corrections neatly.

Test Preparation

Students perform better on formal assessments when they are well prepared for the testing situation. Here are some things you can do before a test to help your students do their best work.

- Explain the nature of the test to students.
- Suggest that they review the questions at the end of the lessons and the unit.
- Remind students to get a good night's sleep before the test.
- Discuss why they should eat a balanced meal beforehand.
- Encourage students to relax while they take the test.

Performance Assessment

Teachers today have come to realize that the multiple-choice format of traditional tests, while useful and efficient, cannot provide a complete picture of students' growth in science. Standardized multiple-choice tests cannot fully reveal how students *think and do things*—an essential aspect of science literacy. Performance assessment can provide this missing information and help balance your assessment program. Well-constructed performance assessments provide a window through which teachers may view students' thought processes.

An important feature of performance assessment is that it involves a hands-on activity in which students solve a situational problem. Students often find performance assessment more enjoyable than traditional paper-and-pencil tests. Another advantage is that it models good instruction: students are assessed as they learn and learn as they are assessed.

Performance Assessment in *ScienceFusion*

Performance tasks can be found in two locations in *ScienceFusion*. In the **Teacher Edition,** a brief performance task is part of the information that accompanies each Review. In this **Assessment Guide,** a more comprehensive task follows each Unit Test. Both types of performance tasks will provide insights into students' ability to apply key science inquiry skills and concepts taught in the unit.

Administering Performance Tasks

Unlike traditional assessment tools, performance assessment does not provide standardized directions for its administration or impose specific time limits on students, although a suggested time frame is offered as a guideline. The suggestions that follow may help you define your role in this assessment.

- ***Be prepared.***
  A few days before students begin the task, read the Teacher's Directions and gather the materials needed.
- ***Be clear.***
  Explain the directions for the task; rephrase them as needed. Also, explain how students' performance will be evaluated. Show students the rubric you plan to use, and explain the performance indicators in language your students understand.
- ***Be encouraging.***
  Your role in administering the assessments should be that of a coach—motivating, guiding, and encouraging students to produce their best work.
- ***Be supportive.***
  You may assist students who need help. The amount of assistance needed will depend on the needs and abilities of individual students.

- ***Be flexible.***
  Not all students need to proceed through the performance task at the same rate and in the same manner. Allow students adequate time to do their best work.
- ***Involve students in evaluation.***
  Invite students to join you as partners in the evaluation process, particularly in development or modification of the rubric.

Rubrics for Assessing Performance

A well-written rubric can help you score students' work accurately and fairly. Moreover, a rubric gives students a better idea of what qualities their work should exhibit before they begin a task.

Each performance task in the program has its own rubric. The rubric lists performance indicators, which are brief statements of what to look for in assessing the skills and understandings that the task addresses. A sample rubric for a task in this **Assessment Guide** follows.

Scoring Rubric

Performance Indicators

______ Assembles the kite successfully.

______ Carries out the experiment daily.

______ Records results accurately.

______ Makes an accurate chart and uses it to report the strength of wind observed each day.

Observations and Rubric Score

3 2 1 0

Scoring a Performance Task

The scoring system used for performance tasks in this **Assessment Guide** is a 4-point scale that is compatible with those used by many state assessment programs. You may wish to modify the rubrics as a 3- or 5-point scale. To determine a student's score on a performance task, review the indicators checked on the rubric and then select the score that best represents the student's overall performance on the task.

4-Point Scale			
Excellent Achievement	Adequate Achievement	Limited Achievement	Little or No Achievement
3	**2**	**1**	**0**

How to Convert a Rubric Score into a Grade

If, for grading purposes, you want to record a letter or numerical grade rather than a holistic score for the student's performance on a task, you can use the following conversion table.

Holistic Score	Letter Grade	Numerical Grade
3	A	90–100
2	B	80–89
1	C	70–79
0	D–F	69 or below

Developing Your Own Rubric

From time to time, you may want to either develop your own rubric or work together with your students to create one. Research has shown that significantly improved performance can result from student participation in the construction of rubrics.

Developing a rubric for a performance task involves three basic steps: (1) Identify the inquiry skills that are taught in the unit and that students must perform to complete the task successfully, and identify what understanding of content is also required. (2) Determine which skills and understandings are involved in each step. (3) Decide what you will look for to confirm that the student has acquired each skill and understanding you identified.

Classroom Observation

"Kid watching" is a natural part of teaching and an important part of evaluation. The purpose of classroom observation in assessment is to gather and record information that can lead to improved instruction. In this booklet, you will find an Observation Checklist (p. AG xv) on which you can record noteworthy observations of students' ability to use science inquiry skills.

Using the Observation Checklist

- ***Identify the skills you will observe.***
  Find out which inquiry skills are introduced and reinforced in the unit.
- ***Focus on only a few students at a time.***
  You will find this more effective than trying to observe the entire class at once.
- ***Look for a pattern.***
  It is important to observe a student's strengths and weaknesses over a period of time to determine whether a pattern exists.
- ***Plan how and when to record observations.***
  Decide whether to

  —record observations immediately on the checklist as you move about the room or

  —make jottings or mental notes of observations and record them later.
- ***Don't agonize over the ratings.***
  Students who stand out as particularly strong will clearly merit a rating of *3* ("Outstanding"). Others may clearly earn a rating of *1* ("Needs Improvement"). This doesn't mean, however, that a *2* ("Satisfactory") is automatically the appropriate rating for the rest of the class. For example, you may not have had sufficient opportunity to observe a student demonstrate certain skills. The checklist cells for these skills should remain blank under the student's name until you have observed him or her perform the skills.

- ***Review your checklist periodically, and ask yourself questions such as these:***

  What are the student's strongest/weakest attributes?

  In what ways has the student shown growth?

  In what areas does the class as a whole show strength/weakness?

  What kinds of activities would encourage growth?

  Do I need to allot more time to classroom observation?

- ***Use the data you collect.***
  Refer to your classroom observation checklist when you plan lessons, form groups, assign grades, and confer with students and family members.

Date ______________________________

Rating Scale			
3	Outstanding	1	Needs Improvement
2	Satisfactory		Not Enough Opportunity to Observe

Names of Students / Inquiry Skills												
Observe												
Compare												
Classify/Order												
Gather, Record, Display, or Interpret Data												
Use Numbers												
Communicate												
Plan and Conduct Simple Investigations												
Measure												
Predict												
Infer												
Draw Conclusions												
Use Time/Space Relationships												
Hypothesize												
Formulate or Use Models												
Identify and Control Variables												
Experiment												

Using Student Self-Assessment

Researchers have evidence that self-evaluation and the reflection it involves can have positive effects on students' learning. To achieve these effects, students must be challenged to reflect on their work and to monitor, analyze, and control their own learning—beginning in the earliest grades.

Frequent opportunities for students to evaluate their performance build the skills and confidence they need for effective self-assessment. A trusting relationship between the student and the teacher is also essential. Students must be assured that honest responses can have only a positive effect on the teacher's view of them and that responses will not be used to determine grades.

Two checklists are found in this **Assessment Guide.** One is Self-Assessment—Active Reading: a form that leads students to reflect on and evaluate their role as active readers. The second is the Experiment/Project Summary Sheet—a form to help students describe and evaluate any projects or activities they may have designed or conducted as independent inquiry.

Using Self-Assessment Forms

- ***Explain the directions.***
  Discuss the forms and how to complete them.
- ***Encourage honest responses.***
  Be sure to tell students that there are no "right" responses to the items.
- ***Model the process.***
  One way to foster candid responses is to model the process yourself, including at least one response that is not positive. Discuss reasons for your responses.
- ***Be open to variations in students' responses.***
  Negative responses should not be viewed as indicating weaknesses. Rather, they confirm that you did a good job of communicating the importance of honesty in self-assessment.
- ***Discuss responses with students.***
  You may wish to clarify students' responses in conferences with them and in family conferences. Invite both students and family members to help you plan activities for school and home that will motivate and support students' growth in science.

Name ______________________________

Think About It

Are you an Active Reader? To find out, read each sentence. Does the sentence tell about you? Circle "yes" or "no." If you are not sure, circle the ?.

1. I often stopped to think about what I read. Yes ? No
2. When I did not understand something, I put a ? near it. Yes ? No
3. I followed the directions for Active Reading on each page. Yes ? No
4. I took time to study the pictures. Yes ? No
5. I made notes in my book to help me remember things. Yes ? No
6. I wrote answers for almost everything in Sum It Up! Yes ? No

This is how being an Active Reader helped me.

____

____

This is what I will do to be a more Active Reader next time.

____

____

Name ______________________________

My Experiment/Project

You can tell about your science project or experiment by completing the following sentences.

1. My experiment/project was about ____________________

____

2. I worked on this experiment/project with ____________

____

3. I gathered information from these sources: __________

____

4. The most important thing I learned from doing this experiment/project is ____________________

____

5. I think I did a (an) ____________ job on my experiment/ project because ____________________

____

6. I'd also like to tell you ____________________

____

Name ______________________________

Think About It

Do you keep a Science Notebook? Circle "yes" or "no" to tell about your Science Notebook. If you are not sure, circle the ?.

1. I am making a table of contents in the front of my notebook. Yes ? No
2. I am making an index in the back of my notebook. Yes ? No
3. I write plans for investigations in my notebook. Yes ? No
4. I put notes and drawings in my notebook. Yes ? No
5. I write questions I have about science in my notebook. Yes ? No
6. I use my notebook to help me remember what I have learned. Yes ? No

This is what I like about my Science Notebook.

____

____

This is what I will do to make my Science Notebook better.

____

____

Portfolio Assessment

A portfolio is a showcase for student work, a place where many types of assignments, projects, reports, and writings can be collected. The work samples in the collection provide "snapshots" of the student's efforts over time, and taken together they reveal the student's growth, attitudes, and understanding better than any other type of assessment. However, portfolios are not ends in themselves. Their value comes from creating them, discussing them, and using them to improve learning.

The purpose of using portfolios in science is threefold:

- ***To give the student a voice in the assessment process.***
- ***To foster reflection, self-monitoring, and self-evaluation.***
- ***To provide a comprehensive picture of a student's progress.***

Portfolio Assessment in *ScienceFusion*

In *ScienceFusion*, students may assemble portfolio collections of their work. The collection may include a few required papers, such as tests, performance tasks, lab response pages, and Experiment/Project Evaluation forms.

From time to time, consider including other measures (Science Experiences Record, Self-Assessment—Active Reading, Self-Assessment—My Science Notebook). The Science Experiences Record, for example, can reveal insights about student interests, ideas, and out-of-school experiences (museum visits, nature walks, outside readings, and so on) that otherwise you might not know about. Materials to help you and your students build portfolios and use them for evaluation are included in the pages that follow.

Using Portfolio Assessment

- ***Explain the portfolio and its use.***
  Describe how people in many fields use portfolios to present samples of their work when they are applying for a job. Tell students that they can make their own portfolio to show what they have learned, what skills they have acquired, and how they think they are doing in science.

- ***Decide what standard pieces should be included.***
  Encourage students to identify a few standard, or "required," work samples that they will include in their portfolios, and discuss reasons for including them. The Student Task sheets for the performance assessments in this **Assessment Guide,** for example, might be a standard sample in the portfolios because they show students' ability to use inquiry skills and critical thinking skills. Together with your class, decide on the required work samples that everyone's portfolio will include.

- ***Discuss student-selected work samples.***
  Point out that the best work to select is not necessarily the longest or the neatest. Rather, it is work the student believes will best demonstrate his or her growth in science understanding and skills.

- ***Establish a basic plan.***
  Decide about how many work samples will be included in the portfolio and when they should be selected. Ask students to list on the Guide to My Science Portfolio (p. AG xxiii) each sample they select and to explain why they selected it.

- ***Tell students how you will evaluate their portfolios.***
  Use a blank Portfolio Evaluation Checklist to explain how you will evaluate the contents of a portfolio.

- ***Use the portfolio.***
  Use the portfolio as a handy reference tool in determining students' science grades and in holding conferences with them and family members. You may wish to send the portfolio home for family members to review.

Name ______________________________

My Science Experiences

Date	What I Did	What I Thought or Learned

Name ______________________________

My Science Portfolio

What Is in My Portfolio	Why I Chose It
1.	
2.	
3.	
4.	
5.	
6.	
7.	

I organized my Science Portfolio this way because ______________________________

____

____

____

____

____

Name ______________________ Date __________

Portfolio Evaluation Checklist

Portfolio Evaluation

Aspects of Science Literacy	Evidence of Growth
1. Understands science concepts *(How Scientists Work; Technology; Animals, Plants; Environments; Earth's Resources, Weather and Seasons; Space; Matter; Forces and Energy)*	
2. Uses inquiry skills *(observes, compares, classifies, gathers/ interprets data, communicates, measures, experiments, infers, predicts, draws conclusions)*	
3. Thinks critically *(analyzes, synthesizes, evaluates, applies ideas effectively, solves problems)*	
4. Displays traits/attitudes of a scientist *(is curious, questioning, persistent, precise, creative, enthusiastic; uses science materials carefully; is concerned for environment)*	

Summary of Portfolio Assessment

For This Review			Since Last Review		
Excellent	Good	Fair	Improving	About the Same	Not as Good

Lesson 1 Quiz

What Are Senses and Other Tools?

1. How would you use this science tool?

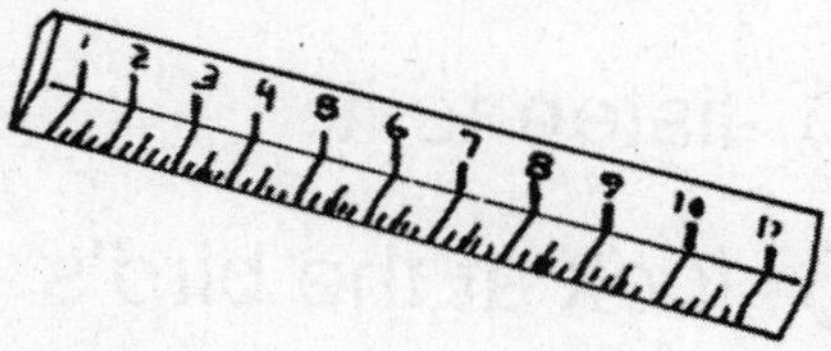

Ⓐ to measure around an object

Ⓑ to measure how long an object is

Ⓒ to measure how heavy an object is

2. What are hearing, sight, smell, taste, and touch?

Ⓐ body parts

Ⓑ feelings

Ⓒ senses

3. Which body part do you use for seeing?

Ⓐ ears

Ⓑ eyes

Ⓒ mouth

4. You want to find out if an apple tastes sweeter than a peach. Which will you use?

Ⓐ ears

Ⓑ hands

Ⓒ mouth

Name ______________________ Date __________

Unit 1

Lesson 2 Quiz

How Can We Use Our Senses?

1. How can you observe the size of this celery?

(A) by looking at it

(B) by smelling it

(C) by tasting it

2. How do you find out how this orange smells?

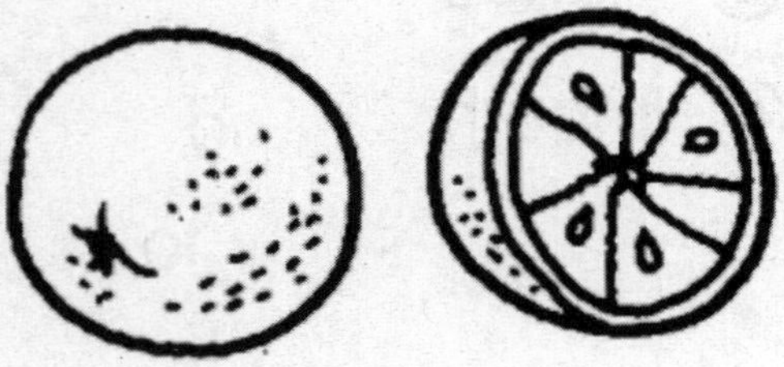

(A) You use your ears.

(B) You use your eyes.

(C) You use your nose.

3. How can you know what sound a bird makes?

(A) listen to it

(B) look at the bird's color

(C) think about what it sounds like

4. How do you compare your observations with a classmate's observations?

(A) make your observations again

(B) think about what you observed

(C) talk about how your observations are alike and how they are different

Name ______________________________ Date __________

What Are Inquiry Skills?

1. Why do scientists use their senses?

   Ⓐ to form an idea

   Ⓑ to get information

   Ⓒ to tell about something

2. Look at these pictures. You observe how these ducks are the same and different.

   What skill are you using?

   Ⓐ communicating

   Ⓑ comparing

   Ⓒ making a model

3. You want to find out what plants need to help them grow. What do you do?

   Ⓐ measure a plant

   Ⓑ draw a conclusion

   Ⓒ plan an investigation

4. What do you do when you infer?

   Ⓐ put things in order

   Ⓑ tell what you think will happen in the future

   Ⓒ use clues and observations to figure out why something happens

Name ______________________ Date __________

How Do We Use Inquiry Skills?

❶ You have a feather and a brick. To learn if weight affects how fast objects fall, what can you ask?

Ⓐ Do soft or hard objects fall faster?

Ⓑ Do light or heavy objects fall faster?

Ⓒ Do large or small objects fall faster?

❷ To know whether plants grow larger in soil or in sand, what do you test?

Ⓐ how soil and sand are alike

Ⓑ which material holds the most water

Ⓒ how the plants grow in sand and in soil

❸ To learn if plants grow larger in soil or in sand, what do you need?

Ⓐ soil and sand

Ⓑ sun and soil

Ⓒ water and sand

❹ One pot has sand. One pot has soil. You put 3 cups of water in each. More water comes out of the pot with sand. What can you record?

Ⓐ Soil holds more water than sand.

Ⓑ Sand holds more water than soil.

Ⓒ Sand and soil hold the same amount of water.

Name ______________________ Date __________

Unit 1

Lesson 5 Quiz

How Do Scientists Work?

1 How do scientists learn more about something?

Ⓐ They investigate it.

Ⓑ They only talk about it.

Ⓒ They only think about it.

2 While doing a test, you collect information. What should you do with this information?

Ⓐ tell a friend

Ⓑ write or draw it

Ⓒ just remember it

3 Look at this picture.

What step in a scientific plan comes **after** the step shown here?

Ⓐ doing a test

Ⓑ asking a question

Ⓒ drawing a conclusion

4 Which is **true** about a hypothesis?

Ⓐ It is a fact.

Ⓑ It can be tested.

Ⓒ It is hard to prove.

Name ______________________ Date ________

How Scientists Work

Vocabulary

❶ What are your five senses?

Ⓐ ear, eye, nose, mouth, and hand

Ⓑ hearing, sight, smell, taste, and touch

Ⓒ singing, looking, sneezing, eating, and holding

❷ What do science tools help people do?

Ⓐ read more quickly

Ⓑ eat healthy meals

Ⓒ find out about things

❸ Which helps you learn about your world?

Ⓐ stating a problem

Ⓑ using inquiry skills

Ⓒ cleaning your area

❹ What is an investigation?

Ⓐ a test that scientists do

Ⓑ a question that scientists ask

Ⓒ a tool that scientists use to measure

Science Concepts

❺ What would you **most likely** show in a chart?

Ⓐ a conclusion

Ⓑ observations

Ⓒ a question

❻ Which tool can you use to observe an object's color, shape, and texture?

Ⓐ balance

Ⓑ hand lens

Ⓒ tape measure

Name ______________________ Date __________

7. Look at this picture.

How do you know whether the lemon is smooth or rough?

Ⓐ by tasting it

Ⓑ by feeling it

Ⓒ by smelling it

8. You draw a picture of what happens in an investigation. Why?

Ⓐ to make observations

Ⓑ to predict what might happen

Ⓒ to share your observations with others

9. You do an investigation. You write observations. Why?

Ⓐ to communicate

Ⓑ to plan

Ⓒ to predict

10. These pictures are in sequence.

How do you know?

Ⓐ They show different groups.

Ⓑ They show how to share ideas.

Ⓒ They show what happens first, next, and last.

Name ____________________ Date __________

11 You want to know whether two identical plants grow larger in soil or in sand. What should be the same?

Ⓐ only the amount of water the plants get

Ⓑ only the amount of sunlight the plants get

Ⓒ the amount of water and the amount of sunlight the plants get

12 What does your nose help you observe?

Ⓐ how something looks

Ⓑ how something smells

Ⓒ how something sounds

13 Look at this picture. You use this tool to find length.

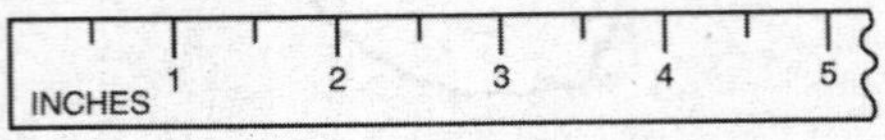

What are you doing?

Ⓐ classifying

Ⓑ inferring

Ⓒ measuring

14 You put two plants into two pots. One pot has sand. One pot has soil. You want to know if the plants grow larger in soil or in sand. What do you do now?

Ⓐ ask a question

Ⓑ draw a conclusion

Ⓒ test your hypothesis

15 You complete an investigation. You use your observations. You tell why you think something happened. What are you doing?

Ⓐ comparing

Ⓑ inferring

Ⓒ predicting

16 Which is **true** about investigating?

Ⓐ There are different ways to investigate.

Ⓑ There is only one right way to investigate.

Ⓒ You must always follow the steps of a scientific plan.

17 You put the same amount of water into two pots. One pot has sand. One pot has soil. More water comes out of the pot with the sand. How can you check your conclusion?

Ⓐ Do the test again.

Ⓑ Ask friends what they think.

Ⓒ Make a different hypothesis and do a different test.

18 What do you do when you draw a conclusion?

Ⓐ tell what you learned from the test

Ⓑ tell what you want to learn from the test

Ⓒ tell what you think will happen during the test

Name ______________________________ Date __________

Inquiry and the Big Idea

Write the answers to these questions.

19 Name two tools you can use during an investigation. What does each one do?

____

____

____

20 Look at this picture. Tell four ways you can use your senses to observe this carrot.

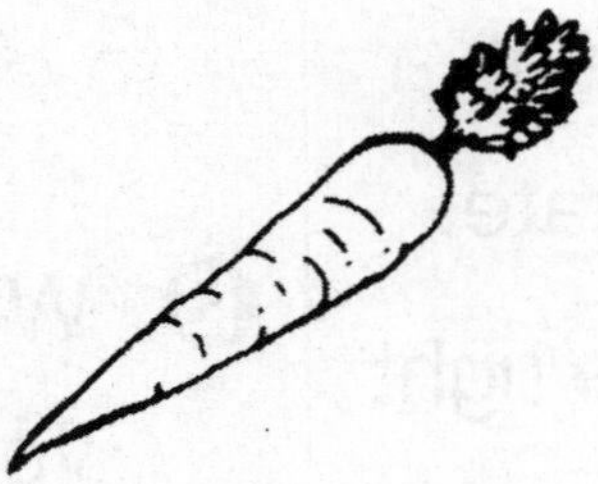

____

____

____

____

Name ______________________ Date __________

What Is It?

Materials

paper, pencil

Procedure

❶ Listen to the teacher describe some classroom objects that are hidden in paper bags. Pay attention to the way the teacher describes how each object looks, feels, sounds, smells, and even tastes.

❷ Use the teacher's descriptions to guess the objects in the bags. Work with a partner to think of as many objects as possible that could fit the descriptions. Write down the names of the objects.

❸ When the teacher shows you the objects, see how many of them you named correctly. Compare the properties of the objects whose names you wrote down to the properties of the objects in the bags. What is similar about them?

What Is It?

Materials Performance Task sheets, various classroom objects, paper bags, paper, pencils

Time 15 minutes

Suggested Grouping pairs

Inquiry Skills compare, infer, communicate, classify

Preparation Hints Find a variety of objects in the classroom, and hide each one in a paper bag. Include objects that have properties that can be described by using the five senses. Give children clues to the identity of each object by describing the way each one looks, feels, sounds, smells, and tastes.

Introduce the Task Remind children that to observe means to gather information by using your senses. Seeing, hearing, smelling, tasting, and touching are senses. To illustrate how many of the senses are used to make thorough observations, challenge children to make observations without using one of their senses, such as the sense of sight. While their eyes are closed, have children feel some objects or listen to their surroundings.

Promote Discussion Have children take turns giving sensory descriptions of objects in the classroom. Direct them to tell how the objects look, feel, sound, smell, and taste, as applicable. You may also have children compare and contrast the qualities of one object to another.

Scoring Rubric

Performance Indicators

______ Makes educated guesses as to the identity of hidden objects, based on sensory descriptions.

______ Effectively works with a partner to generate and write down educated guesses.

______ Compares similarities between educated guesses and the objects in the bag.

Observations and Rubric Score

3 2 1 0

Name ______________________ Date __________

How Do Engineers Work?

1 Carlos is using a tool that he built. What problem does it solve?

Ⓐ Carlos can not reach things on high shelves.

Ⓑ Carlos does not know how to cook.

Ⓒ Carlos can not scratch his back.

2 Ryan plans to build a toy plane that will fly. Which material should he choose?

Ⓐ brick

Ⓑ cotton

Ⓒ paper

3 Jenna designs and tests a pencil holder. Then she thinks of a way to improve it. What step should Jenna do next?

Ⓐ find a new problem

Ⓑ communicate results

Ⓒ redesign the holder to make it better

4 Why are math and science important to engineers?

Ⓐ They help people cure illnesses.

Ⓑ They help people solve problems.

Ⓒ They help people use different tools.

Name ______________________ Date __________

How Can We Solve a Problem?

1. Which materials are **best** for building a strong bookshelf?

Ⓐ wood and nails

Ⓑ paper and tape

Ⓒ cardboard and glue

2. Rochelle wants to build a better rake. How can she follow the design process?

Ⓐ buy a new rake

Ⓑ plan a new design

Ⓒ tell a friend about it

3. You use the design process to plan a tool. What should the tool do?

Ⓐ solve a problem

Ⓑ make a problem

Ⓒ tell about a problem

4. Todd has a problem. He can not reach the light switch in his room. He follows the design process to solve the problem.

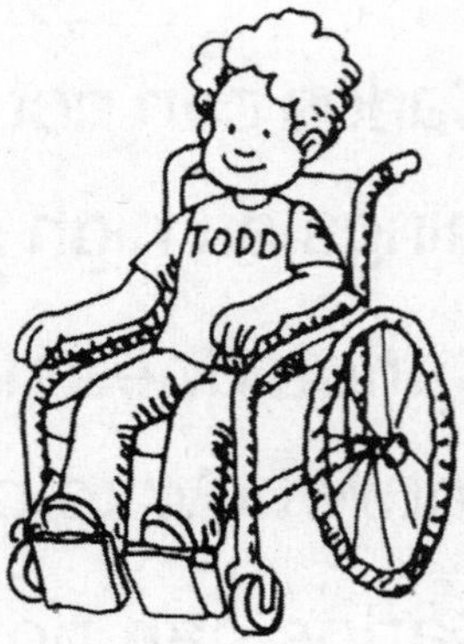

How should Todd keep good records as he works?

Ⓐ brainstorm ideas

Ⓑ choose materials for his plan

Ⓒ draw and write about what he does

Name ______________________ Date __________

What Materials Make Up Objects?

1. What kinds of materials do you see in this sandbox?

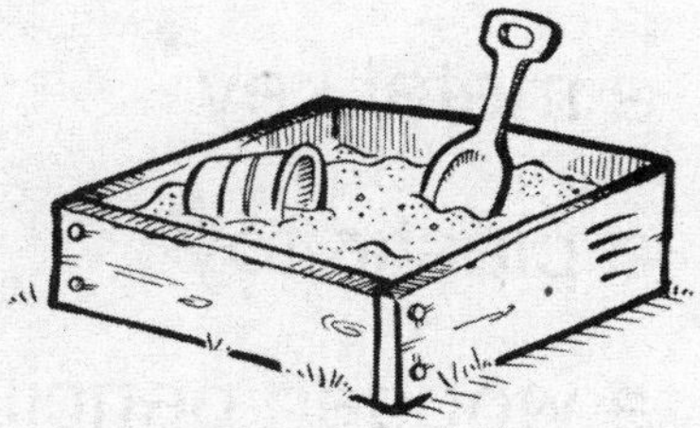

Ⓐ only natural
Ⓑ only human-made
Ⓒ both natural and human-made

2. Which part is needed to make a car?

Ⓐ a booster seat
Ⓑ a handlebar
Ⓒ wheels

3. Which two materials are human-made materials?

Ⓐ cotton and wood
Ⓑ plastic and nylon
Ⓒ wood and plastic

4. Which object is made from a natural material?

Ⓐ a wood bat
Ⓑ a nylon bat
Ⓒ a plastic bat

Name ________________________ Date ________

How Can Materials Be Sorted?

1 Look at this picture.

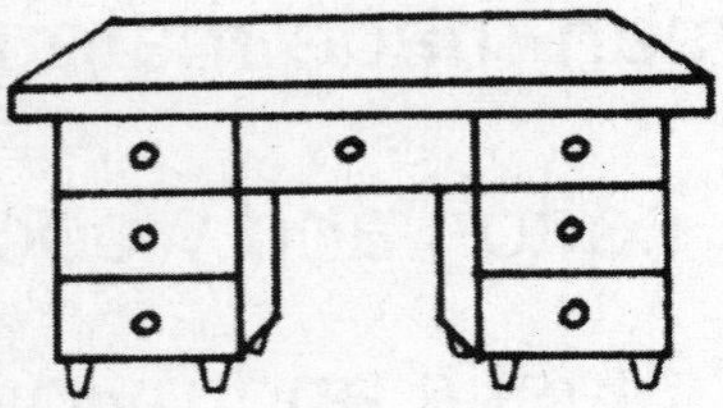

What natural material is the desk made from?

Ⓐ nylon

Ⓑ paper

Ⓒ wood

2 Kim's necklace is made of cotton and wood. What kinds of materials make up the necklace?

Ⓐ only natural

Ⓑ only human-made

Ⓒ both natural and human-made

3 Which of these comes from a human-made material?

Ⓐ a metal key

Ⓑ a plastic toy

Ⓒ a wooden pencil

4 Look at this picture. The balloon is plastic. The string is nylon.

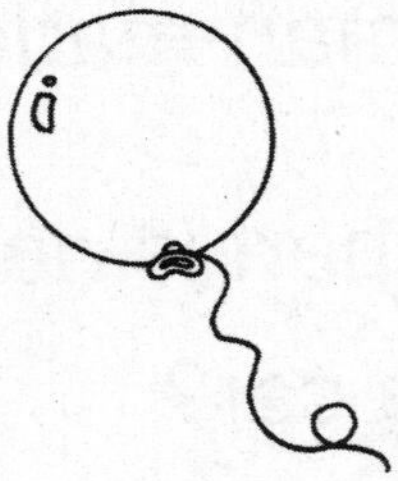

What kinds of materials make up the object?

Ⓐ only natural

Ⓑ only human-made

Ⓒ both natural and human-made

Name ______________________ Date __________

Unit 2

Unit Test

Technology All Around Us

Vocabulary

1. Where do natural materials come from?

   Ⓐ classrooms
   Ⓑ labs
   Ⓒ nature

2. What are materials made by people called?

   Ⓐ engineer-made
   Ⓑ human-made
   Ⓒ nature-made

3. What is a plan with steps that help engineers solve problems?

   Ⓐ the design process
   Ⓑ the engineer process
   Ⓒ the scientist process

4. What do engineers do?

   Ⓐ cure illnesses
   Ⓑ predict weather
   Ⓒ solve problems

5. What makes up objects?

   Ⓐ materials
   Ⓑ science
   Ⓒ words

Science Concepts

6. Which lists two steps of the design process in the correct order?

   Ⓐ 1. communicate
   2. redesign

   Ⓑ 1. redesign
   2. find a problem

   Ⓒ 1. find a problem
   2. plan and build

❼ Henry plans and builds this paper airplane.

What should he do next?

Ⓐ test his design

Ⓑ find a new problem

Ⓒ choose new materials

❽ Mr. Levy builds a fence around his yard. What problem does he solve?

Ⓐ His dog will not stay in the yard.

Ⓑ His dog will not eat all of its food.

Ⓒ His dog will not fetch a stick in the yard.

❾ Look at this picture. Kia has a problem with her little brother.

What problem does Kia need to solve?

Ⓐ how to teach her brother to walk

Ⓑ how to keep her brother from crawling

Ⓒ how to keep her brother from opening cabinets

❿ Which of these comes from a natural material?

Ⓐ a nylon kite

Ⓑ a glass bowl

Ⓒ a plastic toothbrush

11. Anita used the design process to make a paper airplane. Anita tested the plane. But it did not fly far. What should she do next?

(A) keep good records

(B) throw the plane away

(C) talk about ways to improve it

12. Angeli has a box filled with toys. What can she do to put the toys made from natural materials into one pile?

(A) use a scale to weigh the toys

(B) use a ruler to measure the toys

(C) use observations to sort the toys

13. Why should you brainstorm different solutions?

(A) Only one idea can be correct.

(B) The first idea is always wrong.

(C) Some solutions may be better than others.

14. This mailbox is metal. The post is wood. The flag is plastic.

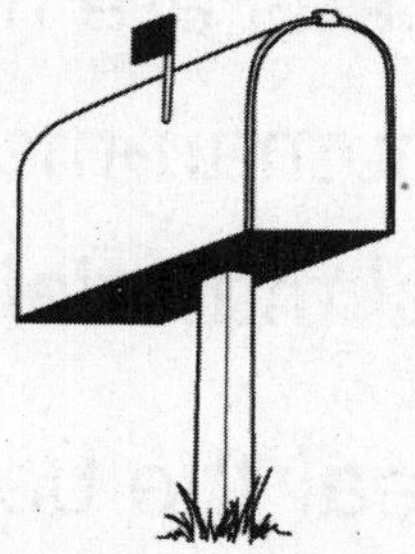

Which part comes from a human-made material?

(A) the flag

(B) the mailbox

(C) the post

Name ______________________ Date __________

15 Which is made of both natural and human-made materials?

Ⓐ a wooden chair with metal legs

Ⓑ a plastic chair with wooden legs

Ⓒ a cotton cloth chair with wooden legs

16 Inez has a string of beads. What can she do to **best** tell whether the beads are made from human-made or natural materials?

Ⓐ wear the beads around her neck

Ⓑ drop a bead to see if it bounces

Ⓒ use her observations and what she knows about materials

17 Lan and Tom plan and build a solution. What should they do next?

Ⓐ find a problem

Ⓑ test and improve

Ⓒ communicate the results

18 Philip uses this table to sort his school supplies. Why does he put plastic paper clips in Group 2?

Group 1: Natural Materials	Group 2: Human-Made Materials
wooden pencil metal paper clips	plastic paper clips nylon backpack

Ⓐ Plastic is natural.

Ⓑ Plastic is human-made.

Ⓒ Paper clips are always plastic.

Name ______________________ Date __________

Inquiry and the Big Idea

Write the answers to these questions.

19. Olivia's teacher asks the class to design a model car that can roll down a ramp. Tell the next two steps in the design process that Olivia should follow.

____

____

20. Roshan wants to make a paper airplane that will fly across the classroom. Tell why Roshan might need to redesign her airplane. Tell one way that Roshan could communicate her results with the class.

____

____

____

____

Name ______________________________ Date ________

Comparing Bridge Designs

Materials

drinking straws

craft sticks

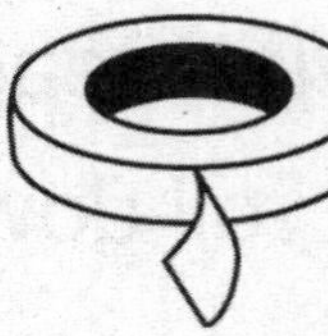
masking tape

glue

yarn

weights

Procedure

1. How can you build the strongest bridge? Think about the problem.
2. Look at the materials. Decide which materials to use to build a bridge.
3. Design a plan to build a model bridge. Draw your design.
4. Build your bridge.
5. Test the strength of your bridge.
6. Record your results. Compare results with your classmates. Draw a picture of the strongest bridge.

Teacher's Directions

Comparing Bridge Designs

Materials Performance Task sheets, drinking straws, craft sticks, masking tape, glue, yarn, a variety of weights

Time 40 minutes

Suggested Grouping small groups

Inquiry Skills make a model, compare, communicate

Preparation Hints Toothpicks, paper clips, and chenille stems can be substituted for craft sticks and drinking straws.

Introduce the Task Show children pictures of different bridge designs. Point out that a bridge is built to support a load. Work together as a class to develop criteria for testing the bridges. Distribute the Performance Task sheets. Ask children to read the directions aloud. Note that the steps closely follow the design process. Make sure children understand each step before proceeding.

Promote Discussion Discuss the importance of having approved criteria for judging the designs. Lead children to understand that results would not be comparable if each group used different criteria to test its bridge. Encourage groups to think of ways to improve upon the best design.

Scoring Rubric

Performance Indicators

______ Identifies a problem and selects appropriate materials to build a model bridge.

______ Plans a design and builds a model bridge.

______ Uses approved criteria to test the strength of the bridge.

______ Improves and redesigns the bridge to make it stronger.

Observations and Rubric Score

3 2 1 0

Name ______________________ Date __________

What Are Living and Nonliving Things?

1 Which is a living thing?

Ⓐ air

Ⓑ a cat

Ⓒ water

2 Which are nonliving things?

Ⓐ animals

Ⓑ plants

Ⓒ toys

3 What do all living things need?

Ⓐ food and water

Ⓑ food, air, and space

Ⓒ food, water, air, and space

4 Which word means to make other things like itself?

Ⓐ grow

Ⓑ live

Ⓒ reproduce

Name ______________________ Date __________

What Do Animals Need?

Lesson 2 Quiz

1 Which of these is a basic need of all animals?

Ⓐ rocks

Ⓑ sand

Ⓒ water

2 Which is **true**?

Ⓐ All animals need oxygen.

Ⓑ Animals do not need oxygen.

Ⓒ Only land animals need oxygen.

3 How is this cow meeting its basic needs?

Ⓐ by breathing air

Ⓑ by drinking water

Ⓒ by finding shelter

4 Which of these living things has the same basic needs as people?

Ⓐ a flower

Ⓑ a shark

Ⓒ a tree

Name ______________________ Date __________

How Are Animals Different?

1 What is **true** about animals?

Ⓐ Animals all move in the same way.

Ⓑ Animals all have the same body coverings.

Ⓒ Animals can have different shapes and body parts.

2 What does this picture tell you about mammals?

Ⓐ Mammals have gills.

Ⓑ Mammals have wings.

Ⓒ Mammals have fur or hair.

3 What body covering do birds have?

Ⓐ feathers

Ⓑ fur

Ⓒ scales

4 Look at these pictures.

How are reptiles and fish alike?

Ⓐ They both have scales.

Ⓑ They both live on land and in water.

Ⓒ They both have fins to help them swim.

Name ________________________________ Date __________

Unit 3

Lesson 4 Quiz

How Can We Group Animals?

❶ In which group does this animal belong?

Ⓐ animals that fly

Ⓑ animals with gills

Ⓒ animals with four legs

❷ In which group do **both** of these animals belong?

Ⓐ animals that fly

Ⓑ animals with legs

Ⓒ animals with spots

❸ Lin is classifying animals. He makes a group called **Animals That Live on Farms**. Which animal goes in that group?

Ⓐ tiger

Ⓑ horse

Ⓒ polar bear

❹ Which animal belongs in the group **Animals That Live in Water**?

Ⓐ 

Ⓑ 

Ⓒ 

Name ______________________ Date __________

Animals

Vocabulary

1 What are living things?

Ⓐ air and space

Ⓑ food and water

Ⓒ people, animals, and plants

2 What is it called when living things make new living things like themselves?

Ⓐ changing

Ⓑ growing

Ⓒ reproducing

3 What is something that most mammals have?

Ⓐ feathers

Ⓑ fur or hair

Ⓒ scales

4 Look at this picture. A nest is a place where birds can be safe.

What is a nest an example of?

Ⓐ an animal

Ⓑ a plant

Ⓒ a shelter

5 What is made up of all living things and nonliving things in a place?

Ⓐ basic needs

Ⓑ an environment

Ⓒ a shelter

❻ What do insects have?

Ⓐ gills

Ⓑ a hard shell

Ⓒ smooth, wet skin

Science Concepts

❼ What will happen to an animal that does not get food, air, and water?

Ⓐ It will find shelter.

Ⓑ It will grow.

Ⓒ It will not be healthy.

❽ To which group do **both** of these animals belong?

Ⓐ animals with gills

Ⓑ animals with wings

Ⓒ animals with feathers

❾ Which is a nonliving thing?

Ⓐ

Ⓑ

Ⓒ

❿ To what group does this animal belong?

Ⓐ birds

Ⓑ insects

Ⓒ reptiles

Name ______________________ Date __________

⓫ Which is true about **most** amphibians?

Ⓐ Amphibians have soft fur.

Ⓑ Amphibians have soft scales.

Ⓒ Amphibians have smooth, wet skin.

⓬ What does this picture show about living things?

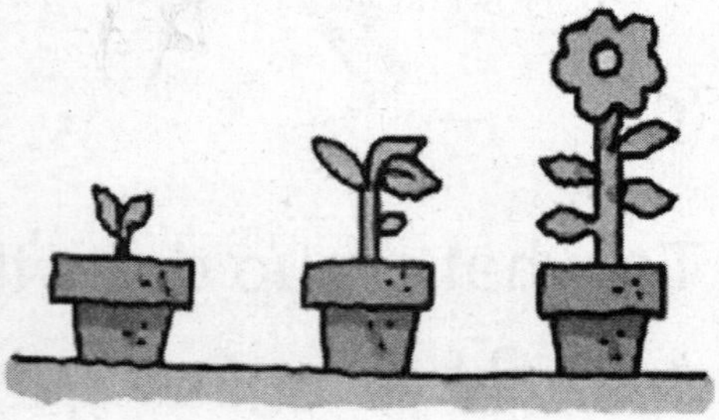

Ⓐ They reproduce.

Ⓑ They grow and change.

Ⓒ They need water and air.

⓭ Why do animals need food?

Ⓐ to breathe

Ⓑ to find a safe place to live

Ⓒ to grow and stay healthy

⓮ Look at this picture.

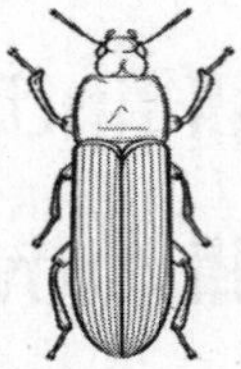

In which group does this animal belong?

Ⓐ animals with fur

Ⓑ animals with gills

Ⓒ animals with six legs

Name ______________________ Date __________

15 What do both of these living things need to live?

Ⓐ air

Ⓑ rocks

Ⓒ soil

16 What does this picture tell you about animals?

Ⓐ All animals are tall.

Ⓑ Animals can be different sizes.

Ⓒ Animals can have different body parts.

17 Which body part helps a fish move through water?

Ⓐ fins

Ⓑ gills

Ⓒ scales

18 Which shows animals in an environment?

Ⓐ

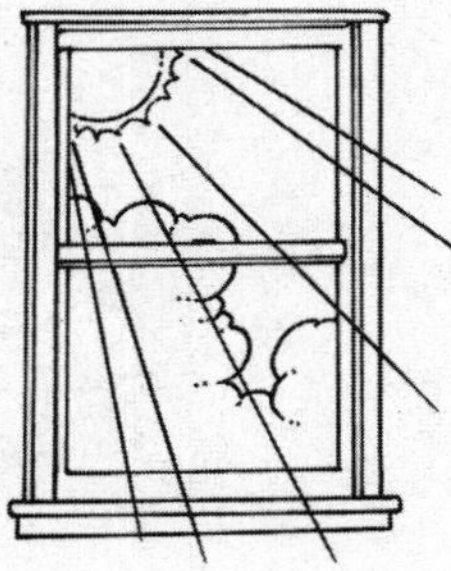

Ⓑ

Ⓒ

Name ______________________ Date __________

Inquiry and the Big Idea

Write the answers to these questions.

19 Tell two ways all of these living things are alike.

____

____

20 Look at this environment. Name two living things you see. Name two nonliving things. Tell how you know.

____

____

____

____

Name ______________________________ Date __________

Student Task

Is It Living or Nonliving?

Materials

index cards

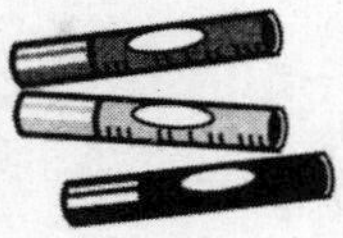

crayons or markers

pencil

Procedure

1. Take five index cards. On each card, draw a picture of a living thing.
2. On the back of each card, write how you know the thing you drew is living.
3. Take five more index cards. On each card, draw a picture of a nonliving thing.
4. On the back of each card, write how you know the thing you drew is nonliving.
5. Share your cards with the class. Tell about the living and nonliving things you drew. Explain the differences between living and nonliving things.

Teacher's Directions

Is It Living or Nonliving?

Materials Performance Task sheets, index cards, crayons or markers, pencils

Time 30 minutes

Suggested Grouping individuals or pairs

Inquiry Skills observe, compare, classify, communicate

Preparation Hints Sort the index cards into stacks of ten. Each child or pair of children will need ten cards.

Introduce the Task Have children look around the classroom and name living and nonliving things. Have them explain how they know that each thing is living or nonliving. Ask children to describe what living things need and can do. Distribute Performance Task sheets and materials, and ask children to read the directions aloud with you. Answer any questions that children raise.

Promote Discussion As children share their cards with the class, encourage them to tell how they know that each thing they drew is living or nonliving. After all have shared, ask children to summarize the attributes of living and nonliving things. Record their statements in a two-column table on the board.

Scoring Rubric

Performance Indicators

______ Draws five pictures of living things.

______ Draws five pictures of nonliving things.

______ For each picture, writes one or more accurate statements about the living or nonliving thing.

______ Effectively communicates to the class the differences between living and nonliving things.

Observations and Rubric Score

3 2 1 0

Name ______________________ Date __________

Unit 4

Lesson 1 Quiz

What Do Plants Need?

1. Kara planted bean seeds in her garden. How can Kara help the seeds to grow?

   (A) She can water them.

   (B) She can let weeds grow around them.

   (C) She can keep them away from sunlight.

2. What do plants need to live and grow?

   (A) water only

   (B) water, air, and sunlight

   (C) water, wind, and clouds

3. Which is a reason why plants need sunlight?

   (A) to make water

   (B) to have space to grow

   (C) to make their own food

4. What do plants do to get the light they need?

   (A) move in the wind

   (B) grow toward the sun

   (C) dig deeper into the soil

Name ______________________ Date __________

Why Do Plants Grow?

1 You do a test with four plants of the same kind. Plant 1 gets light and water. Plant 2 gets light but no water. Plant 3 gets water but no light. Plant 4 gets no water and no light. What question could you investigate?

Ⓐ How is water different from light?

Ⓑ How does water help a plant grow?

Ⓒ Do plants need water and light to grow?

2 What will happen if a plant gets no light or water?

Ⓐ It will die.

Ⓑ It will grow.

Ⓒ It will stay the same.

3 This plant gets water and light. Predict what will happen to the plant.

Ⓐ It will die.

Ⓑ It will grow.

Ⓒ It will survive but not grow.

4 You have two plants. What can you do to find out if plants need water to live?

Ⓐ Water both plants.

Ⓑ Water only one plant.

Ⓒ Do not water the plants.

What Are Some Parts of Plants?

❶ Look at this picture.

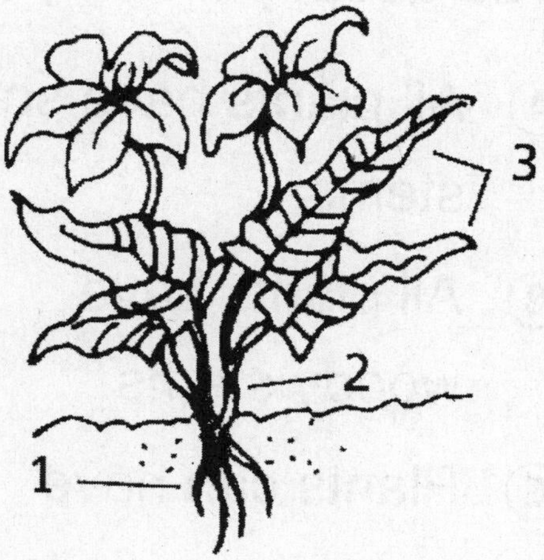

Where is the plant's stem?

Ⓐ Number 1

Ⓑ Number 2

Ⓒ Number 3

❷ What plant part takes in water from the ground?

Ⓐ flowers

Ⓑ roots

Ⓒ stems

❸ What is **true** about leaves?

Ⓐ Leaves can make different seeds.

Ⓑ Leaves all have the same shape and size.

Ⓒ Leaves can have different shapes and sizes.

❹ What do a plant's flowers do?

Ⓐ Flowers make seeds.

Ⓑ Flowers hold up the leaves.

Ⓒ Flowers take in water and sunlight.

Name ______________________ Date __________

How Are Plants Different?

1. Which living thing can make its own food?

   Ⓐ an alligator

   Ⓑ a plant

   Ⓒ a rabbit

2. Look at these plants.

   How are they alike?

   Ⓐ They have the same shape.

   Ⓑ They have one thick, woody stem.

   Ⓒ They have the same kinds of leaves.

3. You can group plants by their stems. Which is **true** about plant stems?

   Ⓐ All plants have soft stems.

   Ⓑ All plants have woody stems.

   Ⓒ Plants can have woody or soft stems.

4. Which sentence about plants is **true**?

   Ⓐ All plants have cones.

   Ⓑ All plants have flowers.

   Ⓒ Some plants have flowers, and some have cones.

Name ______________________ Date __________

How Can We Compare Leaves?

1 What can you measure using paper clips?

Ⓐ the mass of a leaf

Ⓑ the color of a leaf

Ⓒ the length of a leaf

2 Look at this picture.

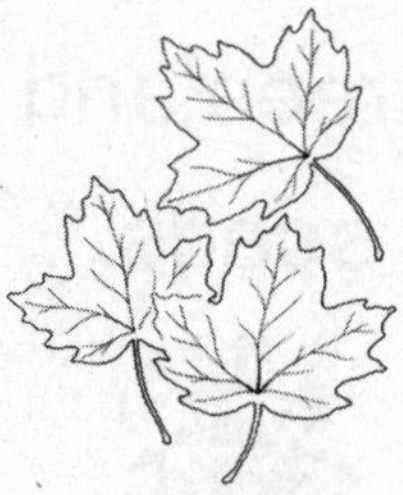

What can you learn about these leaves **without** measuring?

Ⓐ The leaves are all the same width.

Ⓑ The leaves are all the same shape.

Ⓒ The leaves are all the same length.

3 Look at this picture. Jenna measured these leaves.

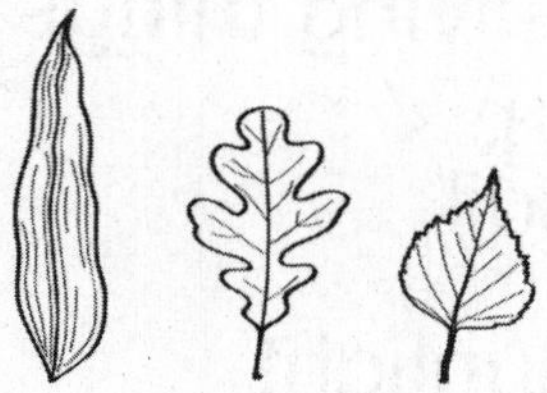

In what order did she put the leaves?

Ⓐ longest to shortest

Ⓑ shortest to longest

Ⓒ lightest to heaviest

4 Look at this table.

Leaf	Length
Leaf 1	5 paper clips
Leaf 2	3 paper clips
Leaf 3	6 paper clips

Which leaf is the longest?

Ⓐ Leaf 1

Ⓑ Leaf 2

Ⓒ Leaf 3

Name ______________________ Date __________

Unit 4

Unit Test

Plants

Vocabulary

❶ What is made up of small pieces of rock and once-living things?

Ⓐ soil

Ⓑ sunlight

Ⓒ water

❷ What are nutrients?

Ⓐ a part of sunlight

Ⓑ parts of a plant's roots

Ⓒ things in soil that help plants grow

❸ What does a plant's stem do?

Ⓐ It holds the seeds.

Ⓑ It holds up the plant.

Ⓒ It makes food for the plant.

❹ Which plant part makes seeds?

Ⓐ flower

Ⓑ leaves

Ⓒ roots

❺ This picture shows something that grows on some trees and holds a plant's seeds.

What is it?

Ⓐ a cone

Ⓑ a leaf

Ⓒ a shrub

Science Concepts

6 A farmer wants to give his plants enough space to grow. What should he do?

Ⓐ plant them far apart

Ⓑ plant them in healthy soil

Ⓒ plant them where the sun shines the most

7 Look at this picture.

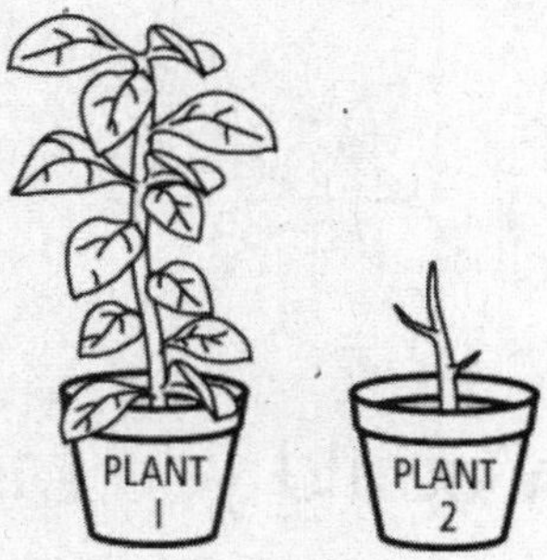

Which plant or plants do you think got light and water?

Ⓐ both plants

Ⓑ Plant 1 only

Ⓒ Plant 2 only

8 Look at these pictures. See how the plant changed.

What caused this change?

Ⓐ The plant needed more air.

Ⓑ The plant needed more space.

Ⓒ The plant grew toward the sun.

9 How do roots help a plant?

Ⓐ Roots hold a plant's seeds.

Ⓑ Roots hold a plant in place.

Ⓒ Roots make food for a plant.

Name ______________________ Date __________

10 You set up an investigation with four plants of the same kind. Plant 1 gets light and water. Plant 2 gets light but no water. Plant 3 gets water but no light. Plant 4 gets no water and no light. What would you predict will happen to the plants?

Ⓐ All plants will grow well.

Ⓑ Plant 1 will grow well.

Ⓒ Plants 1 and 3 will grow well.

11 How does water get from the roots to other parts of the plant?

Ⓐ through the flowers

Ⓑ through the leaves

Ⓒ through the stem

12 Which number points to the roots?

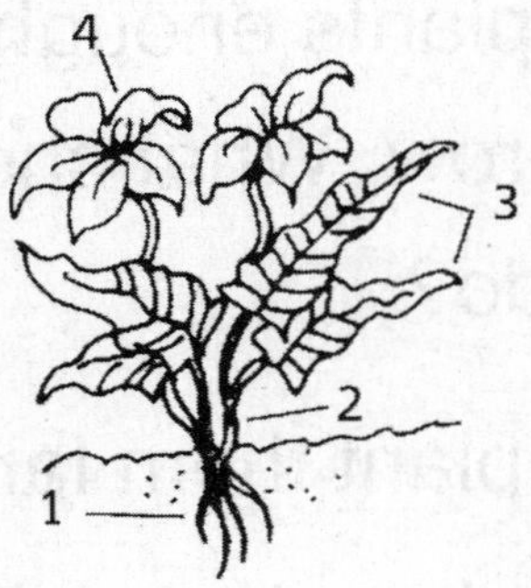

Ⓐ Number 1

Ⓑ Number 2

Ⓒ Number 4

13 Look at this picture.

How could you measure the length of the leaf?

Ⓐ put the leaf on a balance

Ⓑ observe the leaf with a hand lens

Ⓒ put paper clips in a row next to it

14 You set up two plants this way. What do you want to test that plants need?

Ⓐ light

Ⓑ warm air

Ⓒ water

15 Sean measures five leaves. He makes this table.

Leaf 1	Leaf 2	Leaf 3	Leaf 4	Leaf 5
3 paper clips	1 paper clip	3 paper clips	2 paper clips	5 paper clips

Which leaves are **shorter** than Leaf 1?

Ⓐ Leaf 2 and Leaf 3

Ⓑ Leaf 2 and Leaf 4

Ⓒ Leaf 3 and Leaf 5

16 How are fruits and cones alike?

Ⓐ Both hold seeds.

Ⓑ Both make food.

Ⓒ Both hold up plants.

17 What can you tell that this plant has?

Ⓐ soft stems and cones

Ⓑ soft stems and flowers

Ⓒ woody stems and cones

18 What can animals do that plants **cannot** do?

Ⓐ grow and change

Ⓑ make their own food

Ⓒ eat plants and animals

Name ______________________ Date __________ Unit 4

Inquiry and the Big Idea

Write the answers to these questions.

19. Tell two things plants get from the soil. Tell what plant part takes in these two things.

____

____

____

____

20. Plants can be grouped in different ways. Name three main groups for plants. Tell what makes each group different.

____

____

____

____

Name ______________________________ Date __________

Plant Needs

Materials

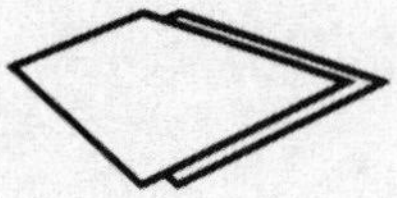
poster board

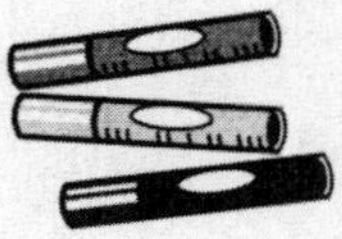
markers

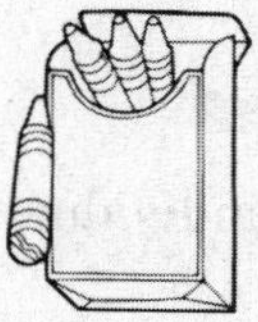
crayons

pencil

Procedure

1. Write the heading **Plants** at the top of the poster board.
2. Draw a plant getting what it needs.
3. Label your drawing to tell what plants need.

Teacher's Directions

Plant Needs

Materials Performance Task sheets, poster board, markers, crayons, pencils

Time 15 minutes

Suggested Grouping individuals or pairs

Inquiry Skills record, communicate

Preparation Hints Have a real plant available for children to observe before they start drawing.

Introduce the Task Have children think about having a plant and what the plant might need each day to live and grow. Distribute the Performance Task sheets and ask children to read the directions aloud with you. Answer any questions that children may raise.

Promote Discussion As children are labeling the needs of plants, encourage them to think about things they need each day to live and grow.

Scoring Rubric

Performance Indicators

_______ Correctly writes heading on the poster board.

_______ Draws a plant meeting all of its needs.

_______ Correctly labels all of the needs of plants.

Observations and Rubric Score

3 2 1 0

Name ____________________ Date __________

Where Do Plants and Animals Live?

❶ Why do many animals need shelter?

Ⓐ It gives them food to eat.

Ⓑ It gives them energy to live.

Ⓒ It gives them a place to be safe.

❷ Which animal lives in an ocean environment?

Ⓐ a fox

Ⓑ a whale

Ⓒ a zebra

❸ These polar bears live in a tundra environment.

Why do they have thick fur?

Ⓐ A tundra is dry.

Ⓑ A tundra is very cold.

Ⓒ A tundra gets a lot of rain.

❹ Which plant would grow **best** in a desert environment?

Ⓐ a cactus

Ⓑ a pine tree

Ⓒ a vine

What Is a Terrarium?

1 Miguel is building a terrarium. He puts in soil, a cap filled with water, and small animals. What else should he add?

Ⓐ fish

Ⓑ plants

Ⓒ toys

2 Which of these shows that animals and plants depend on each other?

Ⓐ an investigation

Ⓑ a shelter

Ⓒ a terrarium

3 Which one provides shelter for a pill bug?

Ⓐ food

Ⓑ leaf cuttings

Ⓒ water

4 What does this terrarium show?

Ⓐ Animals can live without water.

Ⓑ Plants do not need sunlight to grow.

Ⓒ Animals get what they need from their environment.

Name ______________________ Date __________

Unit 5

Unit Test

Environments

Vocabulary

1 What do all the living and nonliving things around you make up?

Ⓐ your environment

Ⓑ your food chain

Ⓒ your shelter

2 What is a place where an animal can be safe?

Ⓐ hilltop

Ⓑ prairie

Ⓒ shelter

3 What shows how energy moves from plants to animals?

Ⓐ an environment

Ⓑ a food chain

Ⓒ a shelter

Science Concepts

4 Where do all living things get energy?

Ⓐ from animals

Ⓑ from machines

Ⓒ from the sun

❺ Look at this picture.

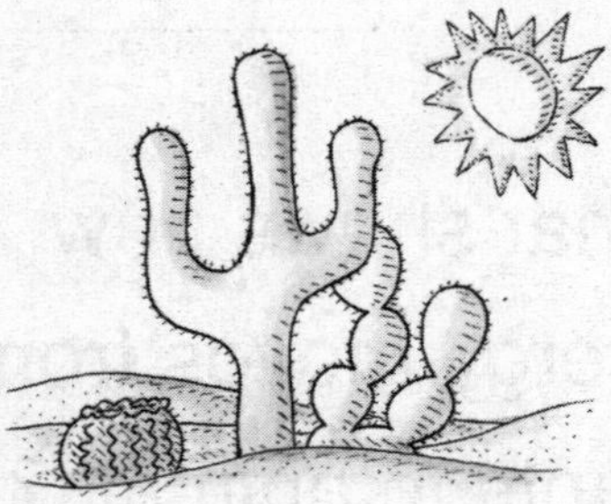

Why does a cactus live in a desert?

Ⓐ A cactus needs a dry environment.

Ⓑ A cactus needs a wet environment.

Ⓒ A cactus needs a cold environment.

❻ This kind of plant grows best in a wet environment.

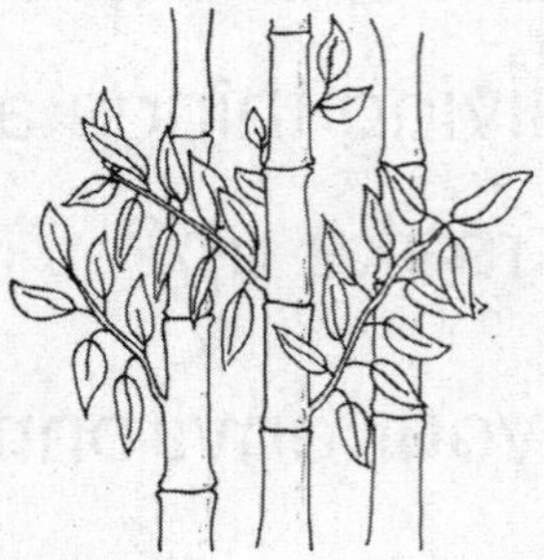

In which environment does the plant **most likely** live?

Ⓐ a desert

Ⓑ a prairie

Ⓒ a rain forest

❼ Which is **true**?

Ⓐ All environments are hot and wet.

Ⓑ Only ocean animals live in shelters.

Ⓒ An animal gets food, water, and shelter from its environment.

Name ______________________ Date __________

8 Which kind of animal lives in a tundra environment?

Ⓐ 

Ⓑ 

Ⓒ 

9 Which is a thing that some animals can use for shelter?

Ⓐ a food chain

Ⓑ sunlight

Ⓒ a tree

10 A desert environment does not get much rain. What helps desert plants to store water?

Ⓐ Desert plants have thick stems or leaves.

Ⓑ Desert plants can move to get closer to water.

Ⓒ Desert plants are short and grow close to the ground.

11 What does the sun provide for a terrarium?

Ⓐ heat and light

Ⓑ soil and water

Ⓒ water and light

Name ______________________ Date ________

⓬ What does a terrarium give plants and animals?

Ⓐ things that make heat

Ⓑ things they need to live

Ⓒ things that produce sound

⓭ Lisa did a project. It showed that plants and animals need each other. It showed they get what they need from their environment.

What was Lisa's project?

Ⓐ a food chain

Ⓑ a model of a desert

Ⓒ a terrarium

Inquiry and the Big Idea

Write the answers to these questions.

14 John sets up a terrarium. He puts in soil, plants, rotten vegetables, and pill bugs. He puts the terrarium in a cool, dark place. Will the terrarium be a good environment for the plants and pill bugs? Why or why not?

____

____

15 Look at this picture.

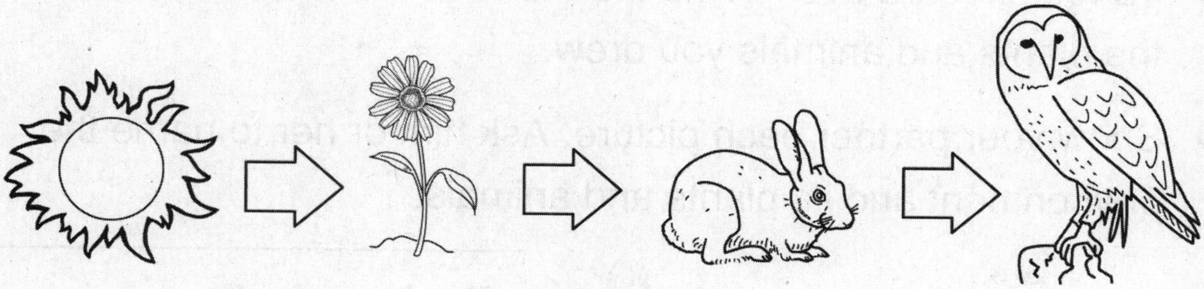

What do the arrows show? Describe the food chain the picture shows.

____

____

____

Name ______________________ Date ________

Unit 5
PERFORMANCE ASSESSMENT

Student Task

Environments

Materials

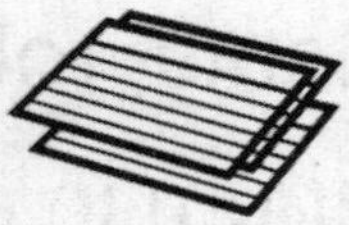

large index cards

crayons or markers

pencil

Procedure

Environments

desert	tundra	ocean	prairie

1. Make a picture card for each environment. Draw plants and animals that belong in the environment.
2. Turn each card over. Write the name of the environment. List the plants and animals you drew.
3. Show your partner each picture. Ask him or her to name the environment and its plants and animals.

Environment

____

Plants and animals

____

____

Environments

Materials Performance Task sheets, large index cards, crayons or markers, pencils

Time 30 minutes

Suggested Grouping individuals and then pairs

Inquiry Skills compare, classify

Preparation Hints Use index cards that are blank on both sides. Display pictures of desert, tundra, ocean, and prairie environments.

Introduce the Task Review the characteristics of desert, tundra, ocean, and prairie environments. Ask children to name plants and animals that live in each. Record children's responses on the board. Distribute the Performance Task sheets and read the directions to children as they follow along. Tell them to work individually to make their cards and to meet with their partner to quiz each other.

Promote Discussion Invite volunteers to share their cards. Encourage them to give specific details about each environment.

Scoring Rubric

Performance Indicators

______ Makes picture cards that accurately depict each environment.

______ Labels each card with the name of the environment and lists plants and animals that are shown.

______ Works cooperatively with a partner.

______ Correctly identifies the environments and the plants and animals shown on the partner's cards.

Observations and Rubric Score

3 2 1 0

Name ______________________ Date __________

What Can We Find on Earth?

1 What is a natural resource?

Ⓐ a pot for a plant

Ⓑ all the things that are in a place

Ⓒ anything from nature that people can use

2 Look at these pictures. Which one is a natural resource?

Ⓐ 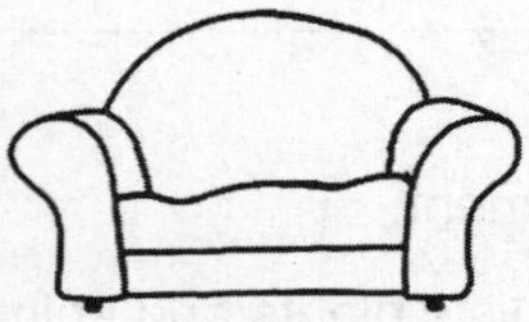

Ⓑ 

Ⓒ 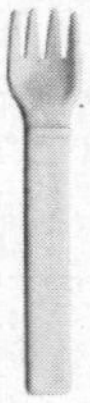

3 Where are natural resources found?

Ⓐ in space

Ⓑ deep below Earth

Ⓒ on or near Earth's surface

4 What natural resource do people use to breathe?

Ⓐ air

Ⓑ soil

Ⓒ water

Name ______________________ Date __________

Unit 6

Lesson 2 Quiz

What Are Rocks and Soil?

1. Which is something that breaks down rock?
   - Ⓐ living things
   - Ⓑ sunshine
   - Ⓒ wind

2. Which word **best** tells a property of the soil you can see in this picture?

   - Ⓐ red
   - Ⓑ rough
   - Ⓒ smooth

3. What things break down to make soil?
   - Ⓐ only bits of rock
   - Ⓑ only once-living things
   - Ⓒ bits of rock and once-living things

4. Which is **true** about water?
   - Ⓐ Water breaks down rock.
   - Ⓑ Water gives rocks a red color.
   - Ⓒ Water changes once-living things into rocks.

Name ______________________ Date __________

Unit 6

Lesson 3 Quiz

What Can We Observe About Rocks?

1 Which senses do you use to observe the texture of rocks?

Ⓐ sight and touch

Ⓑ smell and sight

Ⓒ touch and smell

2 Look at this picture.

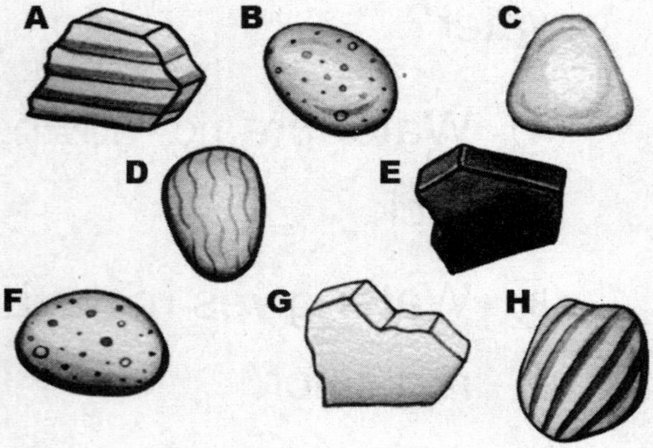

How can you sort these rocks?

Ⓐ by color and size

Ⓑ by size and shape

Ⓒ by shape and color

3 Look at this picture.

How did Jake sort these rocks?

Ⓐ by color

Ⓑ by size

Ⓒ by texture

4 You observe the shape, color, and size of some rocks. What can you do to record what you observe?

Ⓐ draw what you observed

Ⓑ show the rocks to a friend

Ⓒ give the rocks to your teacher

Name ______________________ Date __________

How Do Soils Differ?

1 Which type of soil has the **smallest** bits?

Ⓐ 

Ⓑ 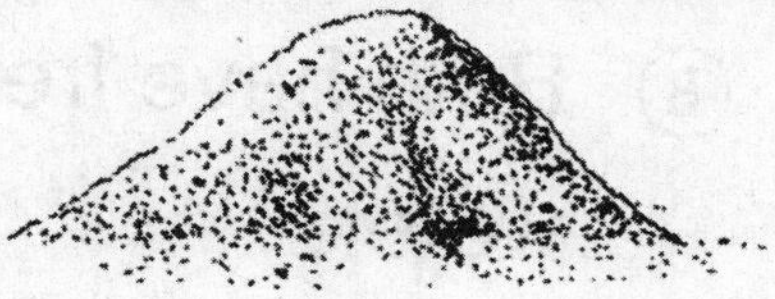

Ⓒ 

2 You draw the once-living things you see in the soil. What do you draw?

Ⓐ bits of rock

Ⓑ drops of water

Ⓒ bits of tree bark

3 Tomas is observing soil samples. He sees that one soil sample is black and the other is brown. What property is Tomas using to describe the soil samples?

Ⓐ the color

Ⓑ the texture

Ⓒ the size of rock bits

4 How does a soil sample with lots of sand in it feel?

Ⓐ rough

Ⓑ smooth

Ⓒ sticky

Name ______________________ Date __________

Where Can We Find Water?

❶ Which is **true** of a lake?

Ⓐ It has land on all sides.

Ⓑ It may flow into an ocean.

Ⓒ It does not have fresh water.

❷ Look at these pictures. Which one shows an ocean?

Ⓐ 

Ⓑ 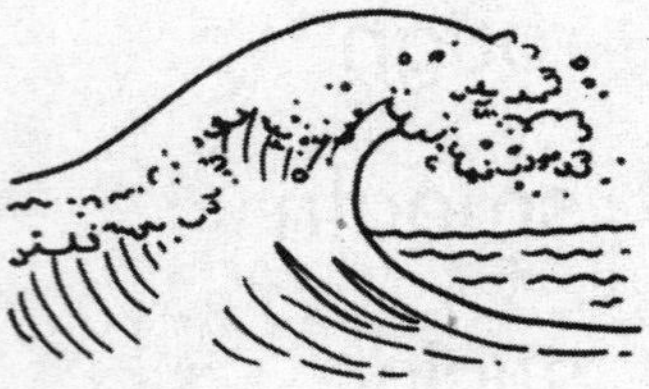

Ⓒ 

❸ How are streams and rivers alike?

Ⓐ Both have huge waves.

Ⓑ Both have fresh water.

Ⓒ Both have water that does not flow.

❹ What do all plants, animals, and people need to live and grow?

Ⓐ grass

Ⓑ sand

Ⓒ water

Name ______________________ Date __________

Unit 6

Lesson 6 Quiz

How Can We Save Resources?

1 What can pollution do?

Ⓐ keep the air clean

Ⓑ make animals sick

Ⓒ help save resources

2 This table shows how many cans a class recycles each day.

Day of the Week	Number of Cans
Monday	16
Tuesday	10
Wednesday	9
Thursday	17
Friday	20

On which days are the **most** cans recycled?

Ⓐ Monday and Tuesday

Ⓑ Tuesday and Friday

Ⓒ Thursday and Friday

3 A caption tells about a picture. What is the **best** caption for this picture?

Ⓐ Bikes cause pollution.

Ⓑ Bikes and cars cause pollution.

Ⓒ You save resources when you ride a bike.

4 How can you reduce your use of resources?

Ⓐ plant a tree

Ⓑ turn off lights

Ⓒ throw trash in a trash can

Name ______________________ Date __________

Earth's Resources

Vocabulary

1. What is soil?
   - Ⓐ the top layer of Earth
   - Ⓑ anything from nature that people can use
   - Ⓒ a hard, nonliving thing that comes from the ground

2. What is a property?
   - Ⓐ something that forms soil
   - Ⓑ a thing that breaks down rock
   - Ⓒ one part of what something is like

3. This picture shows a large body of flowing water.

   What is this body of water?
   - Ⓐ a lake
   - Ⓑ an ocean
   - Ⓒ a river

4. What is a large body of salty water where most of Earth's water is found?
   - Ⓐ a lake
   - Ⓑ an ocean
   - Ⓒ a river

5. What is pollution?

Ⓐ a way to care for resources

Ⓑ waste that harms land, water, and air

Ⓒ something that people use to make products

Science Concepts

6. Which is **true** about natural resources?

Ⓐ They are living things.

Ⓑ They are nonliving things.

Ⓒ They can be living or nonliving things.

7. What can you compare about soils by looking?

Ⓐ color

Ⓑ sound

Ⓒ texture

8. Look at this picture.

Which natural resource moves a windmill?

Ⓐ air

Ⓑ plants

Ⓒ water

9. Look at this picture.

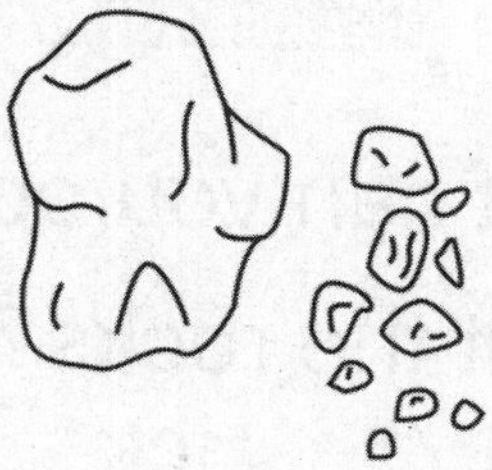

What happens to rock as it breaks down into small bits?

Ⓐ It becomes soil.

Ⓑ It becomes a plant.

Ⓒ It changes its color.

Name ______________________________ Date __________

10 What happens if plants, animals, and people do not have water?

Ⓐ They eat more.
Ⓑ They get bigger.
Ⓒ They cannot live.

11 Look at this picture.

What can you observe about the rocks?

Ⓐ They are all the same size.
Ⓑ They all come from Earth.
Ⓒ They all have the same texture.

12 Look at this picture.

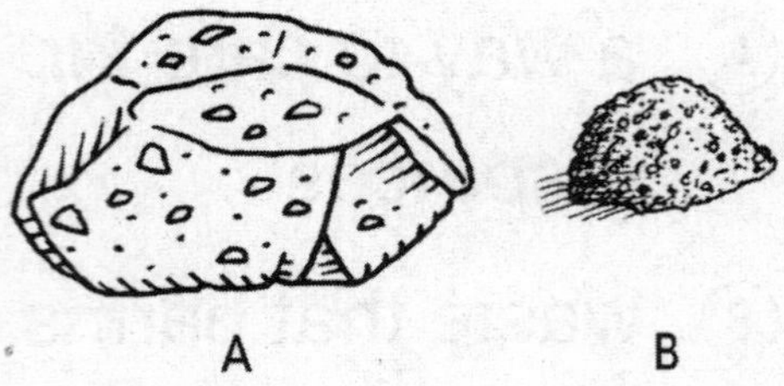

What difference can you observe between the two rocks?

Ⓐ Rock A is larger.
Ⓑ Rock A is harder.
Ⓒ Rock A is smaller.

13 Look at this picture.

What is another way to sort these rocks?

Ⓐ by color
Ⓑ by shape
Ⓒ by texture

14 What makes one soil sample different from another?

- Ⓐ the way the soil is used
- Ⓑ the materials in the soil
- Ⓒ the animals that walk on the soil

15 Look at this picture.

Which water safety rule is the child breaking?

- Ⓐ Learn to swim.
- Ⓑ Never swim alone.
- Ⓒ Wear a life jacket while boating.

16 What gives soil its color?

- Ⓐ the color of the water
- Ⓑ the color of the leaves
- Ⓒ the color of the rock bits

17 Leo observes a sample of soil. How will he use this tool?

- Ⓐ to look at rock bits
- Ⓑ to break up rock bits
- Ⓒ to separate rock bits

18 You use an old towel to wash your bike. What did you do?

- Ⓐ You reused.
- Ⓑ You reduced.
- Ⓒ You recycled.

Name ______________________________ Date __________

Inquiry and the Big Idea

Write the answers to these questions.

19 Compare recycling and reducing. Give an example of each.

____

____

____

____

20 Tell about four ways that you use natural resources every day.

____

____

____

____

Name ______________________________ Date __________

Student Task

Earth's Water

Materials

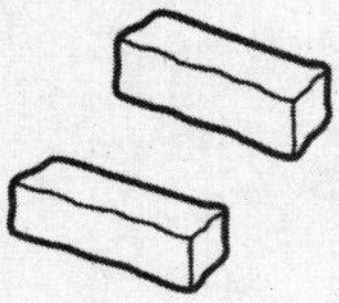
clay

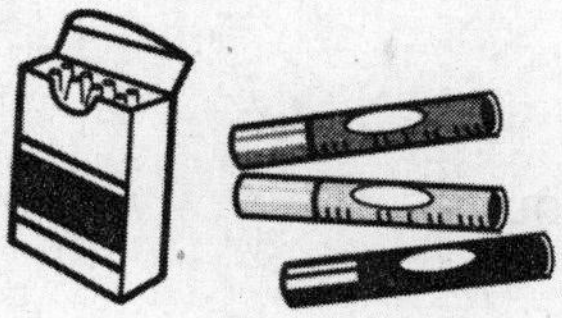
crayons or markers

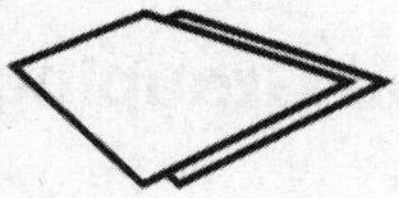
drawing paper

Procedure

1. Think of two bodies of water.
2. Make models of the bodies of water.
3. Draw a picture of each body of water you modeled. Label the kind of water.
4. Share your pictures with the class. Describe the water in your pictures.

Earth's Water

Materials Performance Task sheets, several colors of modeling clay, crayons or markers, drawing paper

Time 30 minutes

Suggested Grouping pairs or small groups

Inquiry Skills compare, make a model, classify

Preparation Hints If possible, show children completed models. Point out that different colors are used for different parts, such as blue for water and brown for land. Make sure that children have blue and brown clay, among other colors. You may wish to make additional materials available to children for their models.

Introduce the Task Ask children to name the types of water presented in the unit. List each type on the board, and discuss the physical characteristics of each. Distribute Performance Task sheets, and ask children to read the directions aloud with you. Answer any questions that children may raise.

Promote Discussion When children finish, have groups share their drawings with the class and describe the characteristics of the water shown. Lead children to recognize general categories, such as "fresh water."

Scoring Rubric

Performance Indicators
______ Constructs accurate models of water. ______ Draws and labels pictures that accurately represent models. ______ Shares drawings of models with the class. ______ Shows an understanding of general categories of water.
Observations and Rubric Score
3   2   1   0

Name ______________________ Date ________

Unit 7

Lesson 1 Quiz

What Is Weather?

❶ What weather does this picture show?

Ⓐ cloudy

Ⓑ hot

Ⓒ windy

❷ Which tool measures temperature?

Ⓐ a rain gauge

Ⓑ a thermometer

Ⓒ a weather report

❸ Why do scientists observe and track weather over time?

Ⓐ to predict the weather

Ⓑ to change the weather

Ⓒ to talk about the weather

❹ Look at this picture.

What is the weather on this day?

Ⓐ cold

Ⓑ hot

Ⓒ rainy

Name ______________________ Date __________

Unit 7

Lesson 2 Quiz

What Can We Observe About Weather?

1 Look at this table. What is the weather on Tuesday?

Mon	Tues	Wed	Thurs	Fri

Ⓐ hot and rainy

Ⓑ hot and sunny

Ⓒ cold and sunny

2 Lee writes down the weather she sees each day. What is Lee doing?

Ⓐ inferring the weather

Ⓑ recording the weather

Ⓒ predicting the weather

3 John says that he thinks the weather in this table happened in summer. Why is John incorrect?

Mon	Tues	Wed	Thurs	Fri
snow 	snow 	sleet 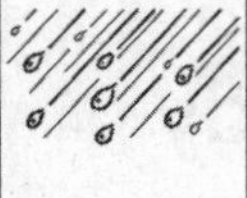	sleet 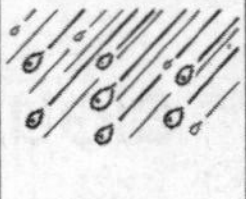	snow 

Ⓐ It is too cold.

Ⓑ It is too dry.

Ⓒ It is too hot.

4 Look at this table. Predict the weather on Saturday.

Mon	Tues	Wed	Thurs	Fri

Ⓐ hot and sunny

Ⓑ cold and sunny

Ⓒ cold and rainy

Name ______________________________ Date __________

What Are Seasons?

❶ Which season is right after spring?

Ⓐ fall

Ⓑ summer

Ⓒ winter

❷ Which season has the fewest hours of daylight?

Ⓐ fall

Ⓑ spring

Ⓒ winter

❸ In which season do plants begin to grow?

Ⓐ fall

Ⓑ spring

Ⓒ summer

❹ Which picture **best** shows the season of fall in most places?

Ⓐ 

Ⓑ 

Ⓒ 

Name ______________________ Date __________

Unit Test

Weather and Seasons

Vocabulary

1. What is moving air called?
   - Ⓐ clouds
   - Ⓑ weather
   - Ⓒ wind

2. What is temperature?
   - Ⓐ the measure of how wet or dry something is
   - Ⓑ the measure of how hot or cold something is
   - Ⓒ the measure of how heavy or light something is

3. What is weather?
   - Ⓐ one of the four seasons
   - Ⓑ what the air outside is like
   - Ⓒ a way to measure temperature

4. What is a season?
   - Ⓐ a time of day
   - Ⓑ a time of year
   - Ⓒ a time of the week

5. What is a weather pattern?
   - Ⓐ stormy weather
   - Ⓑ the warmest weather of the year
   - Ⓒ a change in weather that repeats

Name ______________________ Date __________

Science Concepts

6 What is the weather in this picture?

Ⓐ cloudy

Ⓑ rainy

Ⓒ sunny

7 Karla wants to measure the rain that falls. Which tool will she use?

Ⓐ

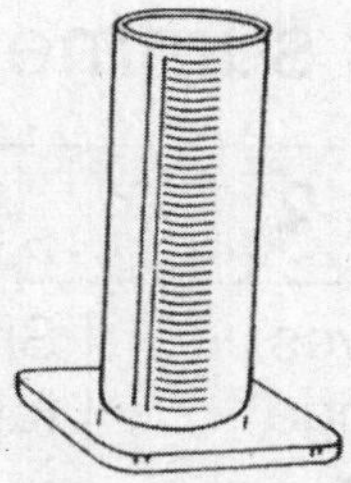

Ⓑ

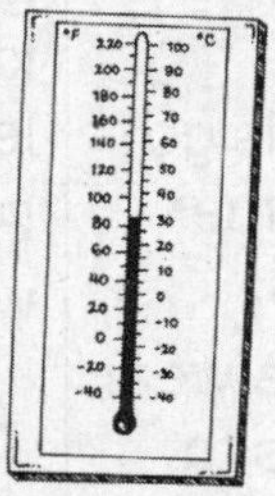

Ⓒ

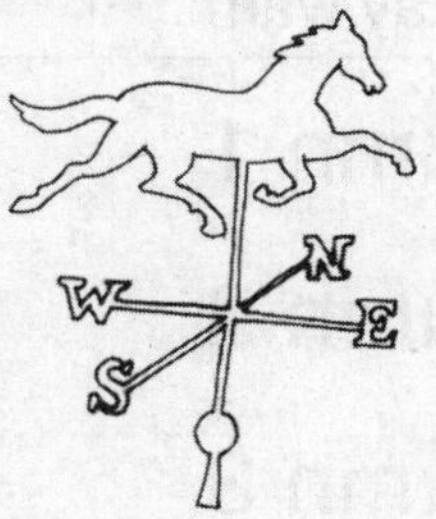

8 Hector listens to the weather report each day. What can he learn?

Ⓐ how to change the weather

Ⓑ how weather was the day before

Ⓒ how to get ready for coming weather

9 What temperature does this thermometer show?

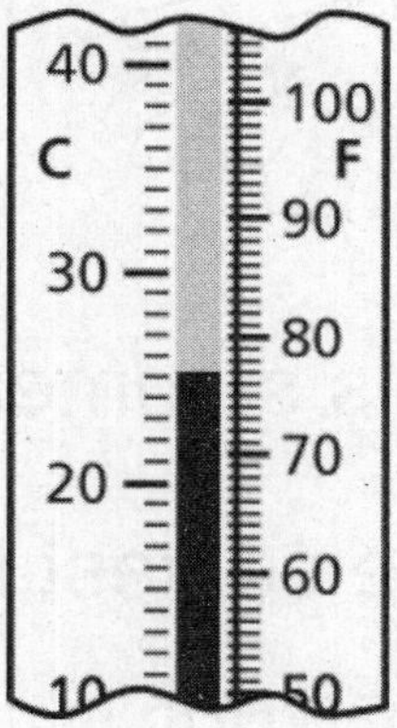

Ⓐ 57 °F

Ⓑ 77 °F

Ⓒ 97 °F

Name ______________________________ Date __________

10 Look at this table.

Mon	Tues	Wed	Thurs	Fri
cloudy cool	rainy cool	sunny clear warm	sunny clear warm	cloudy cool

What would you take to school on Tuesday?

Ⓐ 

Ⓑ 

Ⓒ 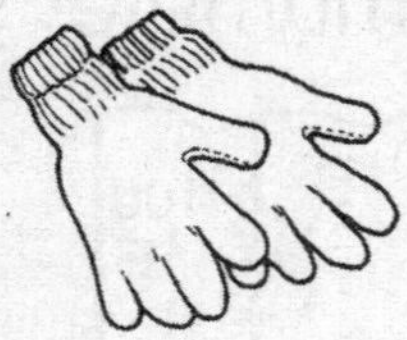

11 What is summer?

Ⓐ the coldest time of the year

Ⓑ the coolest time of the year

Ⓒ the warmest time of the year

12 Infer the season this table shows.

Mon	Tues	Wed	Thurs	Fri
cloudy cool	cloudy cold	snowy cold	snowy cold	cloudy windy cold

Ⓐ spring

Ⓑ summer

Ⓒ winter

13 Tom made this table. Each column describes a season. Which one describes summer?

1	2	3
Many storms occur. Plants grow fruit. People dress to stay cool.	Leaves change color. Some animals go to warmer places. People wear jackets to stay warm.	Snow can fall. Many trees lose their leaves. People wear warm coats.

Ⓐ column 1

Ⓑ column 2

Ⓒ column 3

14 What do some animals do in spring?

Ⓐ They have their young.

Ⓑ They move to warmer places.

Ⓒ They grow more fur to keep warm.

15 Which tree is shown in winter?

Ⓐ 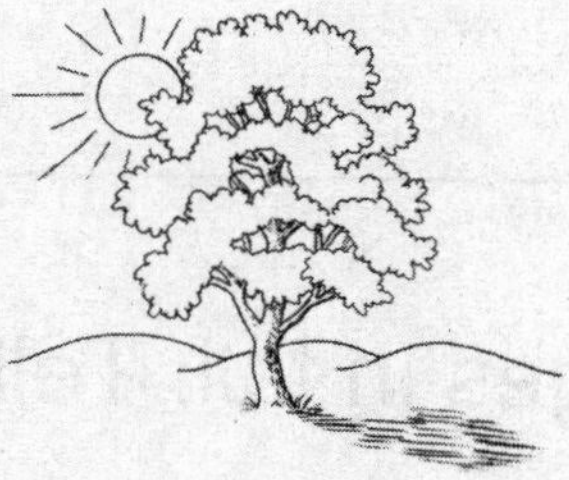

Ⓑ 

Ⓒ 

16 Which season comes right **before** fall?

Ⓐ spring

Ⓑ summer

Ⓒ winter

17 What can you do to try to predict what the weather will be like next week?

Ⓐ ask a friend

Ⓑ look out the window

Ⓒ look at a weather report for this week

18 Which describes winter?

Ⓐ few hours of daylight

Ⓑ more daylight than in fall

Ⓒ the most hours of daylight

Name ______________________ Date __________

Inquiry and the Big Idea

Write the answers to these questions.

19 Which picture shows weather? How do you know?

____

____

20 Tell one way that the weather changes in fall. Tell one way that the seasonal change affects plants, one way that it affects animals, and one way that it affects people.

____

____

____

Name ______________________ Date __________

Picture the Season

Materials

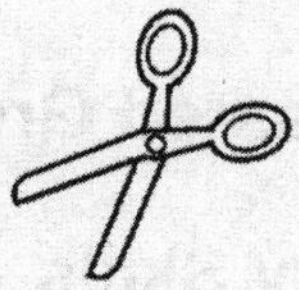

magazines or newspapers	construction paper	glue	scissors

Procedure

1. Choose one of the four seasons.
2. Look through magazines and newspapers for pictures of things that go with that season. Look for ways people are dressed. Look for things that happen outside.
3. Cut out the pictures and glue them to a piece of construction paper.
4. Show your pictures to the class. Have your classmates guess the season you chose.

Teacher's Directions

Picture the Seasons

Materials Performance Task sheets, magazines or newspapers, construction paper, glue, scissors

Time 30 minutes

Suggested Grouping pairs or small groups

Inquiry Skills observe, gather data, interpret data

Preparation Hints To ensure that all four seasons are chosen, write each season on slips of paper and put them in a bag. Have children select a slip. Remind them not to let anyone know what season they have because classmates will have to guess it later.

Introduce the Task Review the four seasons. Ask children to describe what it's like outside during each season. Have them describe how people dress during each season and things they might see in different seasons. Then tell them they will choose one season and will look through magazines and newspapers for pictures of things that show activities people do or clothing people wear during that season. Allow children to also draw pictures to illustrate the season.

Promote Discussion When children finish building their displays, ask them to show the pictures to the class. Have the class guess the season. Then have children explain why each picture belongs with that season. Finally, choose four children who each had a different season. Have them stand randomly in front of the class. Involve the whole class in showing the correct order of the seasons by positioning one of the four children and asking where each of the other children should stand.

Scoring Rubric

Performance Indicators

______ Identifies pictures of things that belong with the season chosen.

______ Makes a display that correctly shows examples of the season chosen.

______ Shows a variety of examples.

______ Explains how each picture belongs with the season chosen.

Observations and Rubric Score

3 2 1 0

Name ______________________ Date ________

What Can We See in the Sky?

Lesson 1 Quiz

1. Which can we see in the daytime sky?
   - Ⓐ the moon and the sun
   - Ⓑ the sun and many stars
   - Ⓒ many stars and the moon

2. Look at these pictures. Which shows a nighttime sky?
   - Ⓐ 
   - Ⓑ 
   - Ⓒ 

3. Which is **true**?
   - Ⓐ There are fewer than 100 stars in the sky.
   - Ⓑ Scientists can easily count all the stars in the sky.
   - Ⓒ There are more stars in the sky than we can easily count.

4. What faraway objects can we use a telescope to see in the night sky?
   - Ⓐ the sun
   - Ⓑ all of the stars
   - Ⓒ the moon and some stars

How Does the Sky Seem to Change?

❶ Which does the sun do?

Ⓐ appears as phases

Ⓑ moves around Earth

Ⓒ warms land, air, and water

❷ What happens as the sun appears to move across the sky?

Ⓐ The sun can change in size.

Ⓑ Shadows can change in size.

Ⓒ Earth changes places with the sun.

❸ What cannot be seen at night?

Ⓐ clouds

Ⓑ stars

Ⓒ the sun

❹ Which of these pictures shows a full moon phase?

Ⓐ 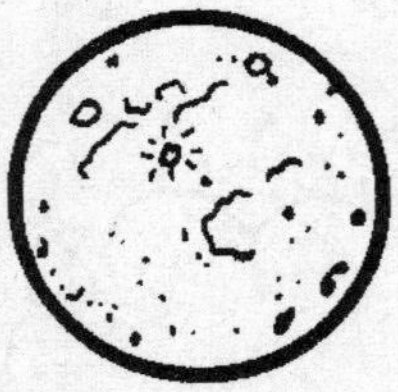

Ⓑ 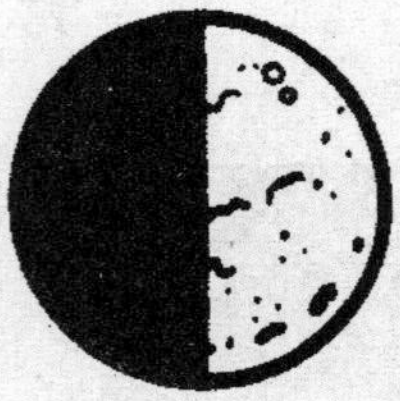

Ⓒ 

Name ______________________ Date __________

How Does the Sun Seem to Move?

❶ Kerry saw this flag. She saw the shadow on the left in the early afternoon. When did she see the shadow on the right?

Ⓐ later in the day

Ⓑ at the same time

Ⓒ earlier in the day

❷ How can Jen measure a shadow without a ruler?

Ⓐ She can try to guess.

Ⓑ She can use an object like a book.

Ⓒ She cannot measure it without a ruler.

❸ Andy wants to see how shadows change each day. Why should he observe shadows on more than one day?

Ⓐ Shadows do not appear every day.

Ⓑ Shadows are hard to see in the daytime.

Ⓒ He wants to be sure results are correct.

❹ How do shadows change throughout the day?

Ⓐ Shadows change place and size.

Ⓑ Shadows change size but not place.

Ⓒ Shadows change place but not size.

Name ______________________ Date __________

Objects in the Sky

Vocabulary

❶ What is an object in the sky that gives off its own light?

Ⓐ cloud

Ⓑ moon

Ⓒ star

❷ What is a large ball of rock that does **not** give off its own light?

Ⓐ cloud

Ⓑ moon

Ⓒ star

❸ What is a dark place made where an object blocks light?

Ⓐ a moon

Ⓑ a phase

Ⓒ a shadow

❹ What is the sun?

Ⓐ a large ball of rock

Ⓑ the star closest to Earth

Ⓒ a sphere that does not give off its own light

❺ Look at this picture of a telescope.

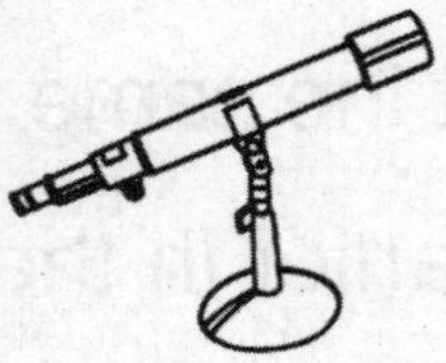

What does this tool do?

Ⓐ helps to remove dark clouds

Ⓑ makes the stars look smaller

Ⓒ helps to magnify things in the sky

❻ What is a phase of the moon?

Ⓐ the shape of the moon we see

Ⓑ the side of the moon that faces Earth

Ⓒ a time when we cannot see the moon from Earth

Science Concepts

❼ Michael sees this phase of the moon in the sky.

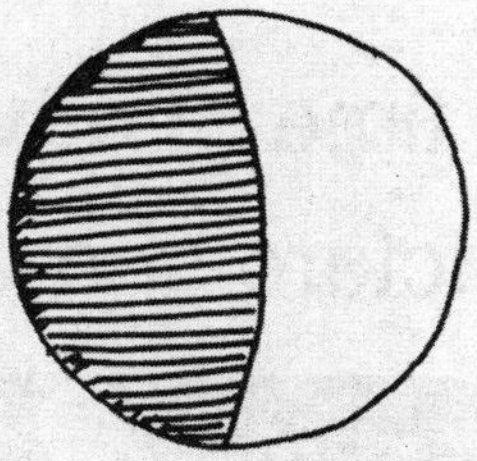

Which phase does Michael see?

Ⓐ first quarter moon

Ⓑ full moon

Ⓒ new moon

❽ Which objects can only be seen in a daytime sky?

Ⓐ 

Ⓑ 

Ⓒ 

❾ Look at this picture. It is early in the morning.

How will the shadow look later in the morning?

Ⓐ It will be longer.

Ⓑ It will be shorter.

Ⓒ It will look the same.

Name ______________________ Date __________

10 How many stars are in the sky?

(A) about 100

(B) fewer than 100

(C) more than we can easily count

11 Which is **true**?

(A) Stars are scattered unevenly in the sky.

(B) The distances between any two stars are equal.

(C) The stars make an even pattern in the nighttime sky.

12 Where can we see the moon?

(A) only in the day sky

(B) only in the night sky

(C) in both the day sky and the night sky

13 Sharon sees the shadow of this tree change while she is at the park.

Where is the sun?

(A) It is in back of the tree.

(B) It is in front of the tree.

(C) It is to one side of the tree.

14 What time of day does this picture show?

(A) afternoon

(B) morning

(C) night

15 Which is **true** of the sun?

Ⓐ It reflects the light of the moon.

Ⓑ It appears to move across the sky.

Ⓒ It sometimes appears in the nighttime sky.

16 Jules measures his shadow with his sneakers. Mary measures his shadow with her sneakers. Why do they get different results?

Ⓐ They both measured wrong.

Ⓑ Their feet are different sizes.

Ⓒ Jules is taller than Mary.

17 Ana's shadow is behind her.

Where is the sun?

Ⓐ behind her

Ⓑ in front of her

Ⓒ right over her head

18 Sarah sees a group of stars in the winter. She does not see them in the summer. Why?

Ⓐ Stars are always moving.

Ⓑ The clouds are blocking the stars.

Ⓒ You can see different groups of stars in different seasons.

Inquiry and the Big Idea

Write the answers to these questions.

19. Suppose there were no sun. Would there be phases of the moon? Explain.

____

____

20. Think about the sun, the moon, and the stars.
Which faraway objects can we see in the day sky?
Which faraway objects can we see only in the day?
Which faraway objects can we see in the night sky?
Which faraway objects can we see only at night?

____

____

____

____

Name ______________________________ Date __________

Stars in the Sky

Materials

black construction paper

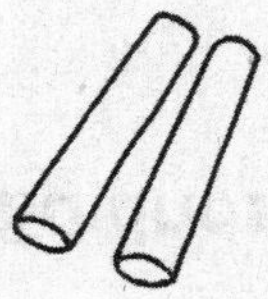

white chalk

Procedure

1. Think about the stars in the nighttime sky.
2. Use the white chalk to draw on black paper what the stars look like in the nighttime sky.
3. Share your drawing with a classmate and tell why you drew the stars the way you did.
4. Discuss whether you were able to draw every star in the sky.

Stars in the Sky

Materials Performance Task sheets, black construction paper, white chalk

Time 15 minutes

Suggested Grouping pairs

Inquiry Skills compare, make a model, communicate

Preparation Hints Have photos of the nighttime sky available if children are having trouble thinking of how stars in the nighttime sky look.

Introduce the Task Prompt children to think about a time when they were outside at night or looking out a window at night. Have them recall how the stars in the sky looked. Lead them to talk about how stars are not evenly spaced and that there are too many stars to easily count. Distribute the Performance Task sheets, and ask children to read the directions aloud with you. Answer any questions that children may raise.

Promote Discussion Have children volunteer to share their *Stars in the Sky* drawing. Encourage them to tell why they drew the stars the way they did.

Scoring Rubric

Performance Indicators

______ Draws many stars scattered on the construction paper.

______ Explains that stars are not evenly spaced in the sky.

______ Shares that there are too many stars in the sky to count or draw.

Observations and Rubric Score

3 2 1 0

Name ______________________ Date __________

What Can We Observe About Objects?

1 You put smooth rocks in one pile. You put rough rocks in another pile. How did you sort the rocks?

Ⓐ by color

Ⓑ by size

Ⓒ by texture

2 Which block is smallest?

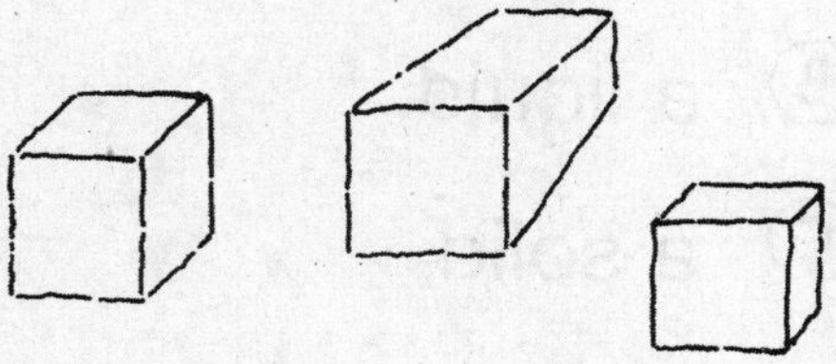

Ⓐ the block on the left

Ⓑ the block in the middle

Ⓒ the block on the right

3 Which object weighs the most?

Ⓐ a desk

Ⓑ paper

Ⓒ a pencil

4 Which of these objects is softest?

Ⓐ 

Ⓑ 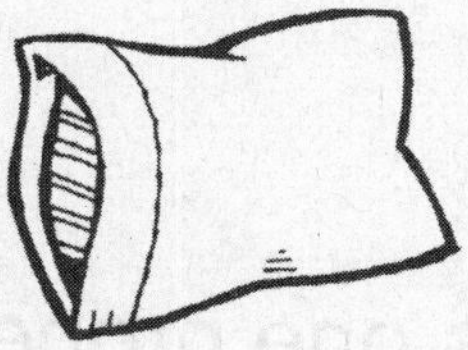

Ⓒ 

Name ______________________ Date __________

What Are Solids, Liquids, and Gases?

1 Which object shows a liquid?

Ⓐ 

Ⓑ 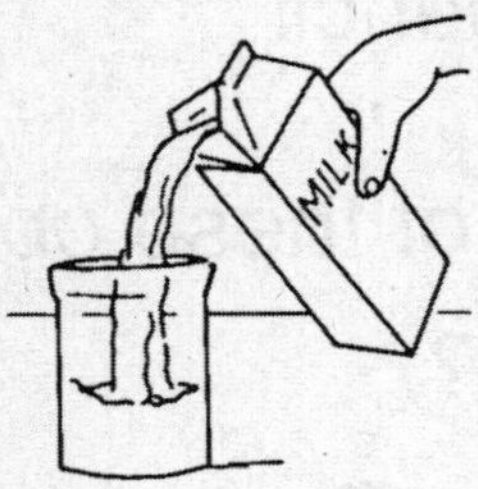

Ⓒ 

2 What is one property of a solid?

Ⓐ It flows.

Ⓑ It fills its container.

Ⓒ It has its own shape.

3 How are solids, liquids, and gases the same?

Ⓐ They all flow.

Ⓑ They are all matter.

Ⓒ They all keep their shape.

4 What kind of matter is a shoe?

Ⓐ a gas

Ⓑ a liquid

Ⓒ a solid

Name ______________________ Date ____________

How Can We Measure Temperature?

1 Which is coldest?

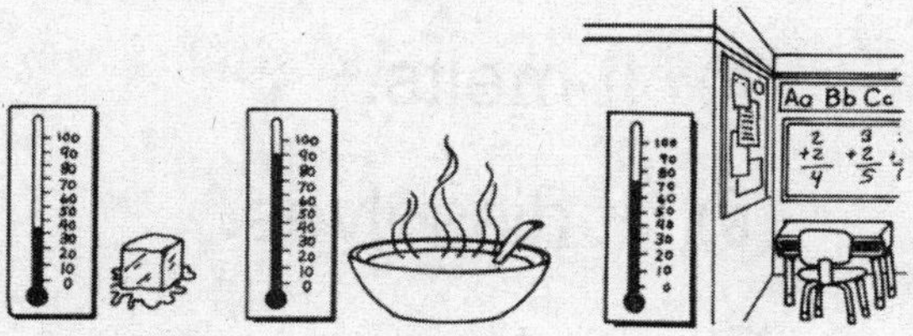

Ⓐ the ice cube

Ⓑ the soup

Ⓒ the classroom

2 You read the temperature of two thermometers. You want to record the information. What should you do with the information?

Ⓐ write it down

Ⓑ think about it

Ⓒ tell it to a friend

3 How do you know that the water in Container A is colder than the water in Container B?

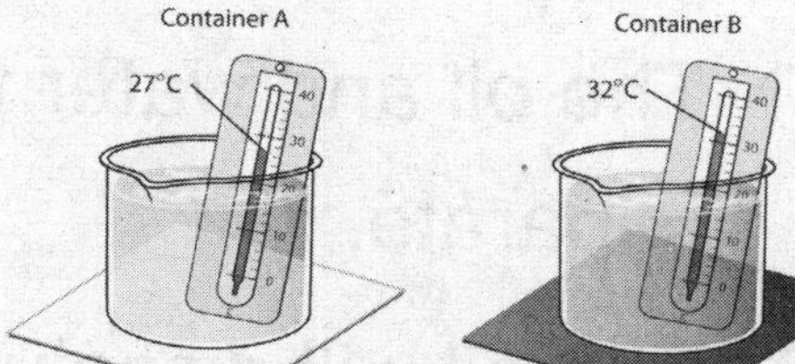

Ⓐ Both temperatures are the same.

Ⓑ The temperature of Container A is lower.

Ⓒ The temperature of Container A is higher.

4 Which is hottest?

Ⓐ an ice cube

Ⓑ a cooked pizza

Ⓒ a ham sandwich

Name ______________________ Date __________

How Can Matter Change?

1 Andrea stirs oil and water in a bowl. What will happen when she stops stirring?

Ⓐ The oil will get hotter.

Ⓑ The oil and water will separate.

Ⓒ The oil will dissolve in the water.

2 What is the result if you add salt to a cup of warm water?

Ⓐ The salt dissolves.

Ⓑ The water disappears.

Ⓒ The salt floats to the top and forms a solid sheet.

3 How does bread change when it is cut?

Ⓐ It melts.

Ⓑ It dissolves.

Ⓒ It changes shape.

4 Look at these pictures. Which shows a mixture?

Ⓐ 

Ⓑ 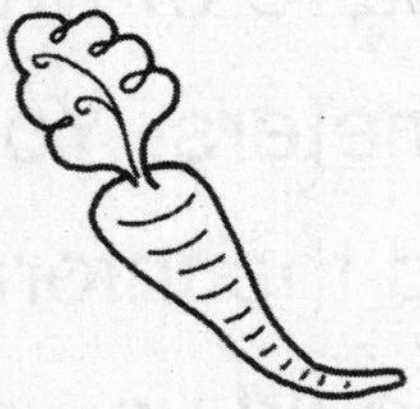

Ⓒ 

Name ______________________ Date __________

Unit 9

Lesson 5 Quiz

What Dissolves in Water?

1. Kara recorded how much time it took sugar to dissolve in warm water.

What I Stirred	Warm Water	Cold Water
sugar	3 minutes	

What is the **best** prediction for how long it will take for sugar to dissolve in cold water?

- (A) 1 minute
- (B) 3 minutes
- (C) 5 minutes

2. You stir sugar into a glass of warm water. What happens?

- (A) The sugar freezes.
- (B) The sugar dissolves.
- (C) All of the sugar sinks to the bottom.

3. Ian stirs sand into a glass of warm water. He knows the sand is **not** dissolving in the water. How does he know?

- (A) The sand melts.
- (B) The sand and water mix completely.
- (C) The sand and water do not mix completely.

4. You do an activity to see how fast different things dissolve in water. How can you record the results for others to see?

- (A) talk about the results
- (B) think about the results
- (C) write the results in a table

Name ______________________ Date __________

All About Matter

Vocabulary

1 What is the only kind of matter that fills all of the space in its container?

(A) gas

(B) liquid

(C) solid

2 What is the amount of matter something has?

(A) mass

(B) solid

(C) space

3 What are size, shape, and color?

(A) properties of matter

(B) ways to change matter

(C) different kinds of mixtures

4 What is matter?

(A) one part of something

(B) anything that takes up space

(C) the way you tell what the world is like

5 What is texture?

(A) what an object feels like

(B) how heavy something feels

(C) how hot or cold something is

❻ What is weight?

Ⓐ what an object feels like

Ⓑ how hot or cold something is

Ⓒ how heavy or light something feels

❼ Which word tells about matter mixing completely with a liquid?

Ⓐ break

Ⓑ dissolve

Ⓒ separate

Science Concepts

❽ What is **true** of all matter?

Ⓐ They have mass.

Ⓑ They are solids.

Ⓒ They are human-made.

❾ How is this boy sorting the objects?

Ⓐ by color

Ⓑ by shape

Ⓒ by texture

❿ Look at this picture. It shows a change you can make to eggs.

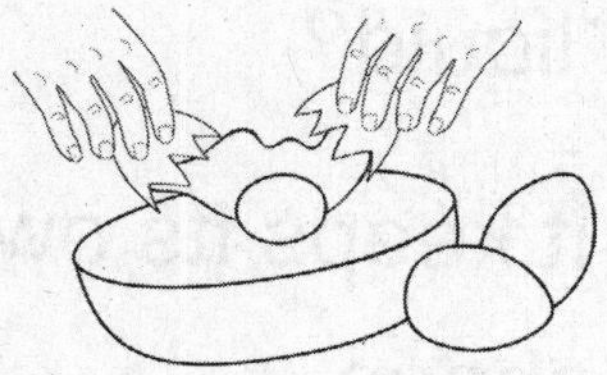

Which describes the same kind of change?

Ⓐ melting ice cubes

Ⓑ breaking a pencil

Ⓒ folding a piece of paper

11 You read the temperature of two thermometers. You want to record the information. What is the **best** thing to do with the information?

- Ⓐ tell a friend about it
- Ⓑ draw your information
- Ⓒ ask your teacher a question

12 Which is one property of a liquid?

- Ⓐ It keeps its own shape.
- Ⓑ It fills the container it is in.
- Ⓒ It takes the shape of its container.

13 In what kind of water will sugar dissolve the **fastest**?

- Ⓐ cold
- Ⓑ cool
- Ⓒ hot

14 José asks a question: Do bread crumbs dissolve in water? What test can he do to answer his question?

- Ⓐ He can weigh the bread crumbs.
- Ⓑ He can stir the bread crumbs in a glass of water and watch what happens.
- Ⓒ He can stir the bread crumbs in a glass of lemonade and watch what happens.

Name ______________________________ Date __________

15 How are liquids and gases alike?

Ⓐ Both need containers.

Ⓑ Both keep their shape.

Ⓒ Both do not have a shape of their own.

16 Which tool helps you sort objects by temperature?

Ⓐ 

Ⓑ 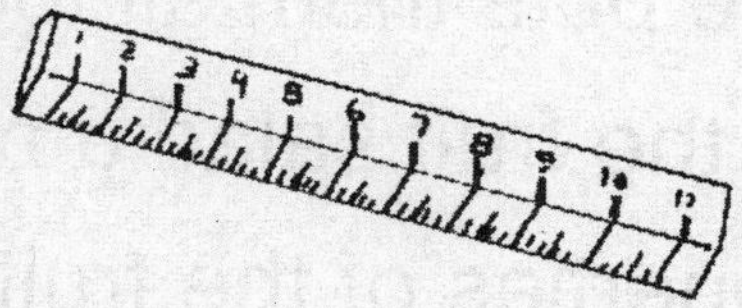

Ⓒ 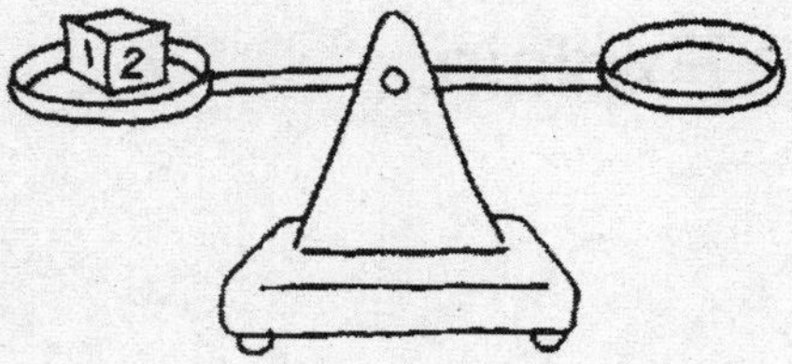

17 Which cup of water is hottest?

Ⓐ Cup 1

Ⓑ Cup 2

Ⓒ Cup 3

18 Which objects float?

Ⓐ the duck and the key

Ⓑ the duck and the boat

Ⓒ the key and the spoon

Name ______________________ Date __________

Inquiry and the Big Idea

Write the answers to these questions.

19 Olivia observes a container at two different times. She sees a change. She uses the clock to measure how long the change takes. What change does Olivia observe? How can Olivia make this change happen faster?

____

____

20 Janel has four kinds of fruit. She puts them all together in one dish to make fruit salad. Is the fruit salad a mixture? Tell why or why not. Do the properties of the fruit change when Janel makes fruit salad? Explain.

____

____

____

Name ______________________ Date __________

Student Task

Comparing Matter

Materials

cotton ball

uncooked macaroni

Procedure

❶ Observe the piece of macaroni and the cotton ball. Look at them and touch them. Write your observations in the chart.

Macaroni		Cotton Ball	
Texture		Texture	
Shape		Shape	
Color		Color	

❷ Are these objects solids, liquids, or gases? Tell how you know.

Comparing Matter

Materials Performance Task sheets, cotton balls, uncooked macaroni

Time 20 minutes

Suggested Grouping pairs

Inquiry Skills observe, compare, infer

Preparation Hints Count out one cotton ball and one piece of macaroni for each pair.

Introduce the Task Tell children that they will compare the properties of two familiar objects: a cotton ball and a piece of macaroni. Ask children to name and discuss the properties of matter, including size, shape, texture, color, and mass. Identify some words children can use to describe these properties, such as *fuzzy* or *smooth* to describe texture. Distribute the Performance Task sheets, and ask children to read the directions aloud with you. Answer any questions children raise. Tell them that they will be working in pairs.

Promote Discussion When children finish, invite them to share their findings and explain their conclusions.

Scoring Rubric

Performance Indicators

______ Observes the properties of the materials and records his or her observations in a chart.

______ Classifies the materials as solids.

______ Demonstrates understanding through explanation of findings and conclusions.

Observations and Rubric Score

3 2 1 0

Name ______________________________ Date __________

How Do Objects Move?

❶ What is motion?

Ⓐ the color of something

Ⓑ the position of something

Ⓒ the movement of something

❷ Look at this picture.

How are the ducks moving?

Ⓐ in a circle

Ⓑ in a zigzag

Ⓒ in a straight line

❸ Look at this picture. The girl and dog started running from the same spot at the same time.

Is the girl or the dog running faster?

Ⓐ The girl is faster.

Ⓑ The dog is faster.

Ⓒ The girl and the dog are running at the same speed.

❹ Which of these do you move back and forth on?

Ⓐ a merry-go-round

Ⓑ a slide

Ⓒ a swing

Name ______________________________ Date __________

How Can We Change the Way Objects Move?

1 Which picture shows force?

Ⓐ 

Ⓑ 

Ⓒ 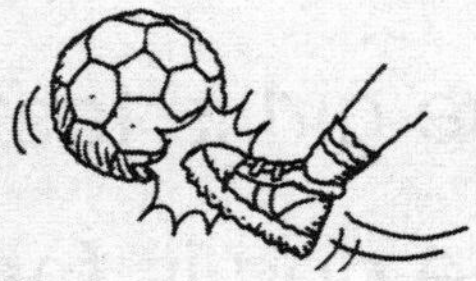

2 What force pulls objects toward Earth?

Ⓐ gravity

Ⓑ a kick

Ⓒ a push

3 Which of these forces is a pull?

Ⓐ kicking a can

Ⓑ throwing a ball

Ⓒ opening a drawer

4 What can change the direction that an object is moving in?

Ⓐ force

Ⓑ position

Ⓒ speed

Name ______________________ Date __________

How Can We Change Motion?

1 You push a toy car. It moves across the floor. How can you record what you see?

Ⓐ You can think about it.

Ⓑ You can write what you see.

Ⓒ You can tell a friend about it.

2 You think that pushing a ball will change its motion. What is the **best** way to know for sure?

Ⓐ take a picture of the ball

Ⓑ push the ball and observe

Ⓒ write a story about the ball

3 You need to choose an object that can hit a ball far. What should you ask?

Ⓐ How was the ball made?

Ⓑ What color should the object be?

Ⓒ What object will put a force on the ball?

4 What question does this picture answer?

Ⓐ Who will catch the ball?

Ⓑ How can I stop the ball's motion?

Ⓒ How can I change the ball's motion?

Name ______________________ Date __________

What Is Sound?

1. Which makes a loud sound to warn you of danger?

Ⓐ 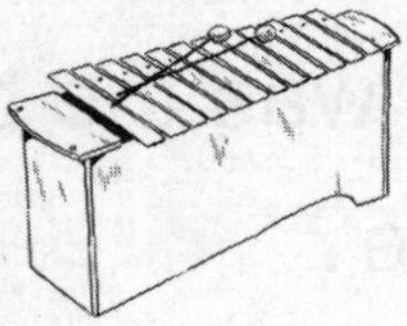

Ⓑ 

Ⓒ 

2. Which is a soft sound?

Ⓐ a person shouting

Ⓑ a fire alarm ringing

Ⓒ a person whispering

3. What must happen for an object to make sound?

Ⓐ The object must vibrate.

Ⓑ The object must get bigger.

Ⓒ The object must get colder.

4. What kind of energy is sound?

Ⓐ energy you hear

Ⓑ energy you see

Ⓒ energy you taste

Name ______________________ Date __________

How Do We Make Sound?

1. In what kind of string does sound travel **best**?

   Ⓐ string that is very loose

   Ⓑ string that is a little loose

   Ⓒ string that is stretched very tight

2. Tamera gathered these materials to make a string telephone.

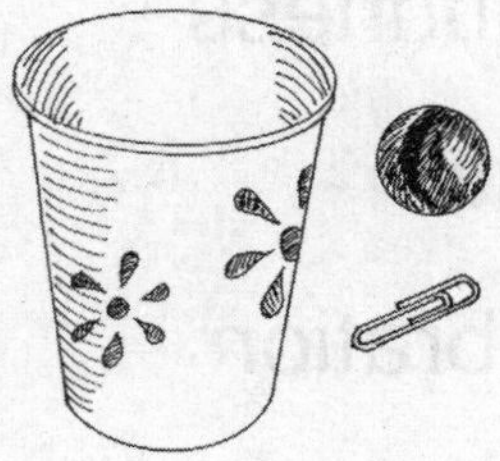

   Which material is not needed?

   Ⓐ a ball

   Ⓑ a cup

   Ⓒ a paper clip

3. Miles made three string telephones for an investigation. One was made with thin string. One was made with thick string. One was made with rope. What did Miles test to find out how sound travels best?

   Ⓐ length of string

   Ⓑ tightness of string

   Ⓒ thickness of string

4. What change happens when sound moves through string?

   Ⓐ The string vibrates.

   Ⓑ The string gets colder.

   Ⓒ The string gets longer.

Name ______________________ Date __________

Forces and Energy

Vocabulary

1. What is speed?

   Ⓐ where something is
   Ⓑ how fast something moves
   Ⓒ the way something changes

2. What makes an object move or stop moving?

   Ⓐ force
   Ⓑ position
   Ⓒ speed

3. What kind of energy can you hear?

   Ⓐ gravity
   Ⓑ light
   Ⓒ sound

4. What does an object do when it vibrates?

   Ⓐ It moves quickly back and forth.
   Ⓑ It moves slowly in one direction.
   Ⓒ It moves quickly in one direction.

5. Which of these tells whether a sound is soft?

   Ⓐ loudness
   Ⓑ pitch
   Ⓒ vibration

Science Concepts

6. Which moves most slowly?

   Ⓐ a bike
   Ⓑ a car
   Ⓒ a train

7 Look at this picture.

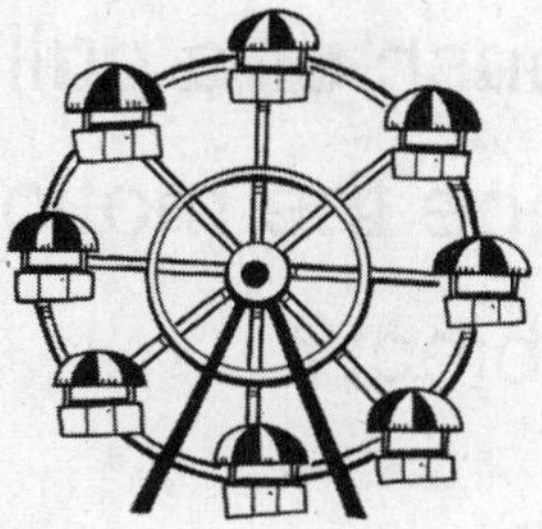

How do the cars on the Ferris wheel move?

Ⓐ round and round

Ⓑ in a straight line

Ⓒ in a zigzag

8 How would you move if you moved in a zigzag?

Ⓐ 

Ⓑ

Ⓒ 

9 Ted uses this table for an investigation. What question is he testing?

How the Cups Are Connected	What Is Heard
metal wire	
string	
plastic fishing line	

Ⓐ How far can sound travel?

Ⓑ Can sound travel through air?

Ⓒ Does sound travel through different materials?

10 What kind of force are the kids using?

Ⓐ pull

Ⓑ push

Ⓒ speed

Name ______________________ Date __________

11 Look at this picture.

What happens when the bat hits the ball?

Ⓐ The ball stops moving.

Ⓑ The ball changes direction.

Ⓒ Forces stop acting on the ball.

12 What question can you ask to find out about how a ball moves?

Ⓐ Where is the ball?

Ⓑ What color is the ball?

Ⓒ How high can I bounce the ball?

13 How can you find out if a push or a pull can change the motion of an object?

Ⓐ You can investigate.

Ⓑ There is no way to know.

Ⓒ You can weigh the object.

14 What question does this picture answer?

Ⓐ What is the ball made of?

Ⓑ How can I make a ball move?

Ⓒ How many kinds of balls are there?

15 Hannah made this table.

Group 1 Kinds of Forces	Group 2 Kinds of Energy	Group 3 Kinds of Motion

Into which group should she put **sound**?

Ⓐ Group 1

Ⓑ Group 2

Ⓒ Group 3

16 Ryan is singing in music class. His teacher asks him to sing a higher note. What is the teacher asking him to do?

Ⓐ sing louder

Ⓑ stop singing

Ⓒ sing a different pitch

17 Adam and Yasmine make a string telephone. The string is 30 inches long. About how far apart should Adam and Yasmine stand to **best** hear sounds through the string telephone?

Ⓐ 10 inches

Ⓑ 20 inches

Ⓒ 30 inches

18 Look at this picture.

What moves the swing?

Ⓐ direction

Ⓑ force

Ⓒ speed

Name ______________________ Date __________

Inquiry and the Big Idea

Write the answers to these questions.

19. You push a cart. What are two ways the force can change the motion of the cart?

____

____

____

____

20. Name the four ways objects can move. Name something that moves in each way.

____

____

____

____

Name ________________________________ Date __________

Unit 10
PERFORMANCE ASSESSMENT

Student Task

How Does It Move?

Materials

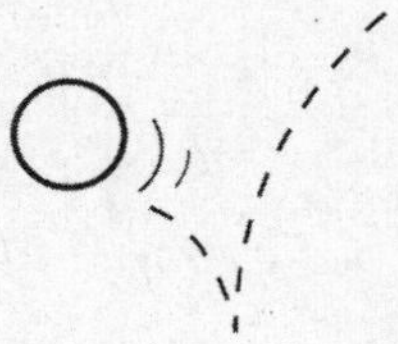
ball

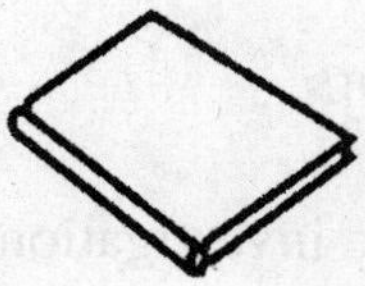
book

pencil

Procedure

1. Jump as far as you can.
2. Lift a ball off the floor. Then drop the ball.
3. Move a book across a desk.
4. Tell what forces made things move. Use this table.

Action	Forces
jump	
lift and drop ball	
move book	

5. Which forces did you use more than once?

____

Teacher's Directions

How Does It Move?

Materials Performance Task sheets, balls, pencils, textbooks

Time 25 minutes

Suggested Grouping individuals or pairs

Inquiry Skills observe, classify, conduct an investigation

Preparation Hints Clear an area for jumping and for bouncing balls.

Introduce the Task Review forces that make things move—pushing, pulling, gravity—and how each functions. Remind children that more than one force may act on an object. Distribute Performance Task sheets, and ask children to read the directions aloud with you. Answer any questions that children raise. Specify terms that children will use to identify forces in the table: *push, pull, gravity*.

Promote Discussion Invite volunteers to share their tables and to identify the forces that caused each movement.

Scoring Rubric

Performance Indicators
_______ Conducts investigation by jumping, lifting and dropping a ball, and moving a book.
_______ For each action, accurately identifies and records the force or forces involved.
_______ Identifies the force or forces that were used more than once.
Observations and Rubric Score
3 2 1 0

Name ______________________ Date __________

End of Year

Cumulative Test A

❶ Look at these pictures.
Which tool can you use to measure how tall a plant is?

Ⓐ 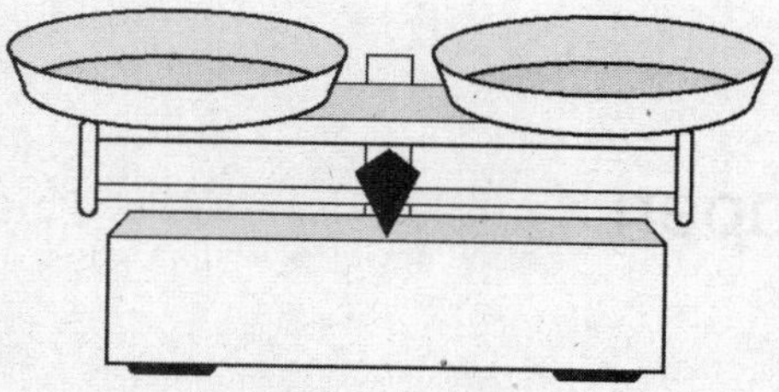

Ⓑ 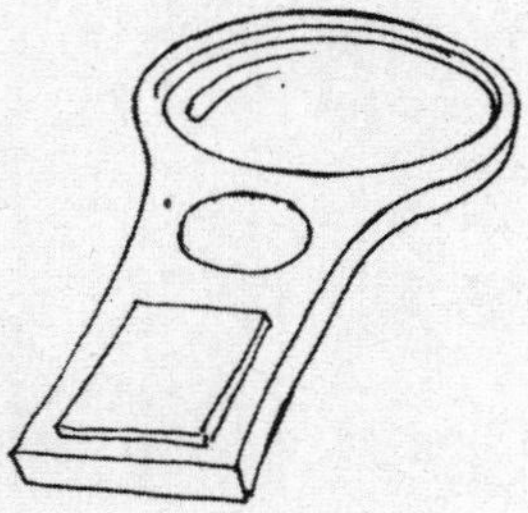

Ⓒ 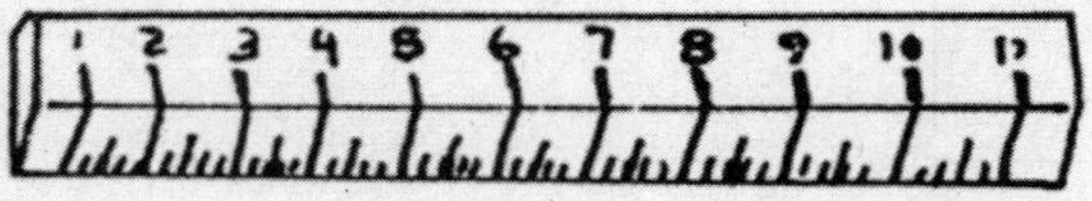

❷ What is the **last** step in the design process?

Ⓐ Communicate

Ⓑ Find a Problem

Ⓒ Test and Improve

3. You do an investigation.
You draw pictures of what happens.
Why?

Ⓐ to record your results

Ⓑ to make observations

Ⓒ to predict what might happen

4. Lindsey made two groups of animals.
Which is the **best** name for Group 1?

Group 1	Group 2
dogs chickens mice	fishes snakes

Ⓐ Animals With Legs

Ⓑ Animals That Swim

Ⓒ Animals With Feathers

❺ Look at this picture.

How are the birds using the tree?

Ⓐ for air

Ⓑ as food

Ⓒ as shelter

❻ Which type of chair is made from human-made materials?

Ⓐ a metal chair

Ⓑ a plastic chair

Ⓒ a wooden chair

❼ A plant does not have enough space.

What will **most likely** happen to the plant?

Ⓐ It will not grow.

Ⓑ It will make fruit.

Ⓒ It will grow larger.

❽ Look at this picture.

What can you tell about this crayon?

Ⓐ It is about 3 paper clips long.

Ⓑ It weighs the same as 3 paper clips.

Ⓒ It is longer than most other crayons.

9 Why do some kinds of owls live in forests?

Ⓐ The owls can not fly to other environments.

Ⓑ The forest environment meets the owls' needs.

Ⓒ There is no room in deserts for these kinds of owls.

10 Soil is made up of many things. Which of these is a part of soil?

Ⓐ boulders

Ⓑ living things

Ⓒ once-living things

Name ______________________________ Date __________

11 Where would you **most likely** find salt water?

Ⓐ in a lake

Ⓑ in an ocean

Ⓒ in a stream

12 Look at this picture.

What kind of pollution is shown?

Ⓐ air pollution

Ⓑ land pollution

Ⓒ water pollution

⑬ Look at this picture.

What is the **best** way to describe the weather?

Ⓐ clear

Ⓑ icy

Ⓒ rainy

⑭ What can a magnifier do?

Ⓐ make the sky darker

Ⓑ make things look bigger

Ⓒ move things to a new place

15 Lourdes observes the weather for four days. She wants to predict the weather on day 5. What should she do first?

Ⓐ Predict weather on day 5.

Ⓑ Record weather for days 1 to 4.

Ⓒ Draw conclusions about weather for days 1 to 4.

16 Which is the correct order of moon phases?

Ⓐ new moon, first quarter moon, full moon

Ⓑ new moon, third quarter moon, full moon

Ⓒ first quarter moon, new moon, third quarter moon

17 Which object weighs the most?

Ⓐ a bicycle

Ⓑ a crayon

Ⓒ paper

18 How do you know that Thermometer C shows the highest temperature?

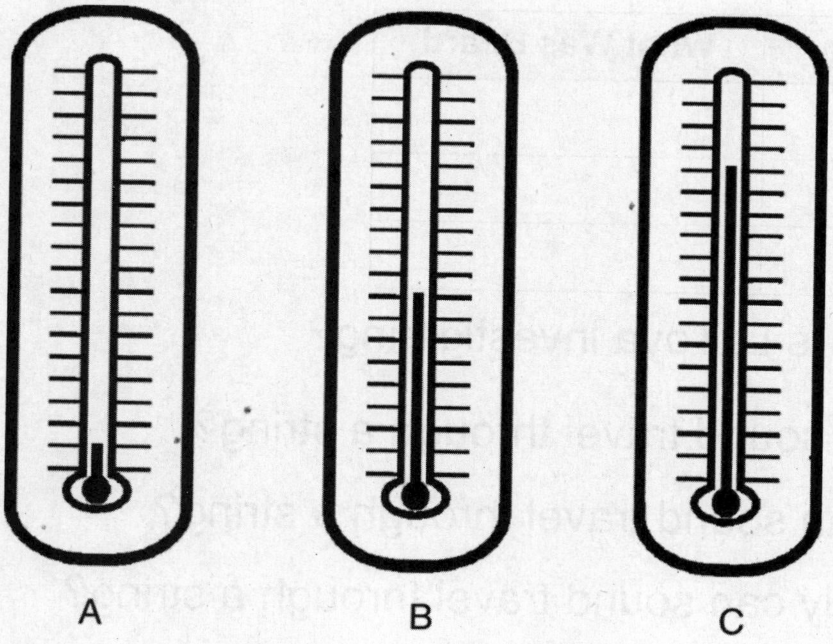

Ⓐ The level on C is the lowest.

Ⓑ The level on C is the highest.

Ⓒ The level on C is lower than A.

19 Which word tells about speed?

(A) fast

(B) motion

(C) zigzag

20 LaToya uses this table to record the results of her investigation.

String Length	What Was Heard
short	
medium	
long	

What question is LaToya investigating?

(A) Can a soft sound travel through a string?

(B) How far can sound travel through a string?

(C) How quickly can sound travel through a string?

Name ______________________________ Date __________

Answer Sheet

Cumulative Test A

Mark one answer for each question.

1 Ⓐ Ⓑ Ⓒ
2 Ⓐ Ⓑ Ⓒ
3 Ⓐ Ⓑ Ⓒ
4 Ⓐ Ⓑ Ⓒ
5 Ⓐ Ⓑ Ⓒ
6 Ⓐ Ⓑ Ⓒ
7 Ⓐ Ⓑ Ⓒ
8 Ⓐ Ⓑ Ⓒ
9 Ⓐ Ⓑ Ⓒ
10 Ⓐ Ⓑ Ⓒ
11 Ⓐ Ⓑ Ⓒ
12 Ⓐ Ⓑ Ⓒ
13 Ⓐ Ⓑ Ⓒ
14 Ⓐ Ⓑ Ⓒ
15 Ⓐ Ⓑ Ⓒ
16 Ⓐ Ⓑ Ⓒ
17 Ⓐ Ⓑ Ⓒ
18 Ⓐ Ⓑ Ⓒ
19 Ⓐ Ⓑ Ⓒ
20 Ⓐ Ⓑ Ⓒ

Name ______________________________ Date __________

End of Year

Cumulative Test B

❶ Look at this picture.

You think Plant A will grow more than Plant B.

What are you doing?

Ⓐ observing

Ⓑ planning

Ⓒ predicting

❷ Which material is human-made?

Ⓐ metal

Ⓑ plastic

Ⓒ wood

❸ Look at these pictures.

You wonder about the properties of these rocks.

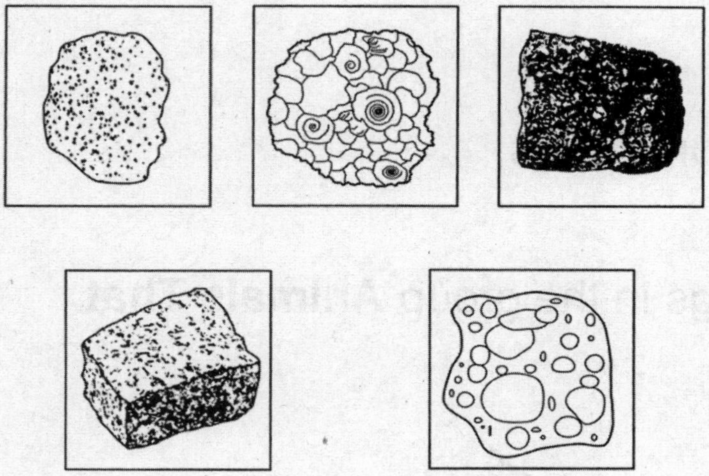

What can you do next to find out more?

Ⓐ ask a question

Ⓑ draw a conclusion

Ⓒ explain the results

❹ What happens to shadows as the day gets closer to noon?

Ⓐ They get longer.

Ⓑ They get shorter.

Ⓒ They stay the same.

5 Why do animals need food, air, and water?

Ⓐ to stay alive

Ⓑ to have shelter

Ⓒ to be different from plants

6 Which animal belongs in the group **Animals That Live on Land**?

Ⓐ 

Ⓑ 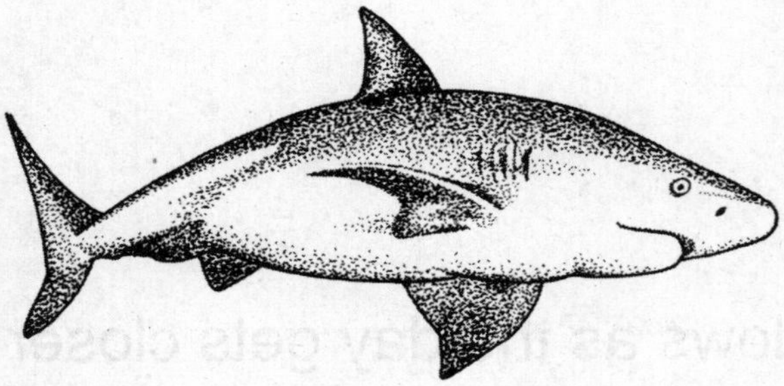

Ⓒ 

❼ What kind of animal has feathers?

Ⓐ a bird

Ⓑ an insect

Ⓒ a reptile

❽ Which part of the plant is the flower?

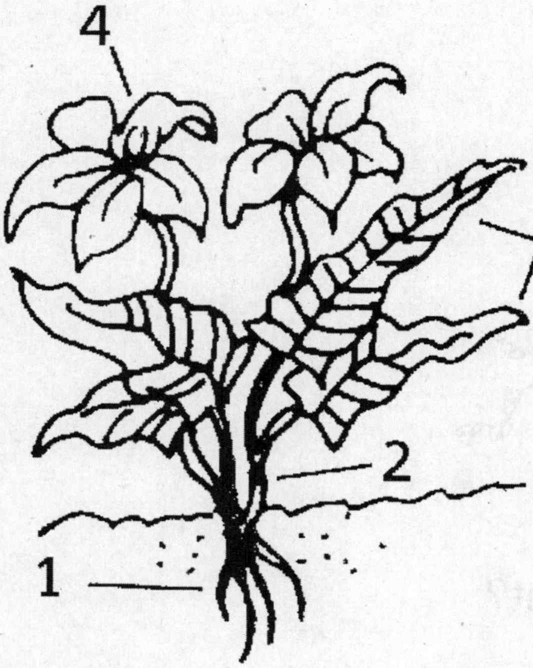

Ⓐ Number 2

Ⓑ Number 3

Ⓒ Number 4

Name ______________________________ Date __________

9 You want to give a plant more space to grow. What should you do?

Ⓐ give it more water

Ⓑ pull up weeds around it

Ⓒ plant more plants around it

10 Look at this picture.

How are these plants different?

Ⓐ Some stems are woody, and some are soft.

Ⓑ Some of the plants do not make their own food.

Ⓒ The plants have different kinds of leaves and flowers.

⓫ Which animal has thick, white fur to help it stay alive in a cold environment?

Ⓐ an arctic fox

Ⓑ a bison

Ⓒ a prairie dog

⓬ Look at these pictures.

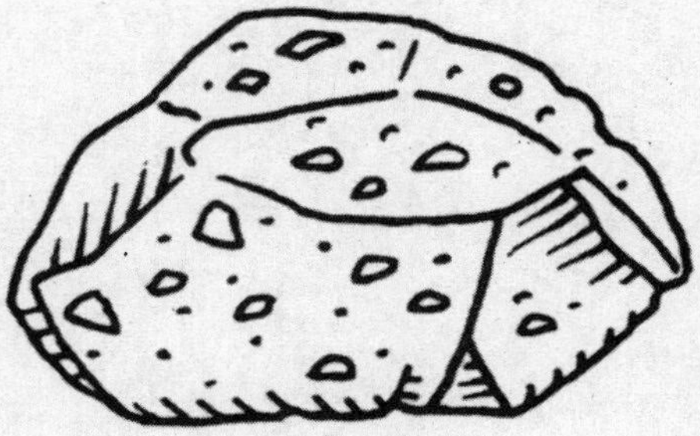

A

B

What do you observe about these rocks?

Ⓐ Rock A is larger than Rock B.

Ⓑ Rock A is smaller than Rock B.

Ⓒ Rock A and Rock B are the same size.

13 Look at these pictures.
Which picture shows people saving resources?

(A) 

(B) 

(C) 

14 Which of these is a solid?

(A) a kite

(B) lemonade

(C) wind

15 How far apart are the stars in the sky?

Ⓐ Stars are all spaced a mile apart.

Ⓑ Stars are spaced evenly from one another.

Ⓒ Stars are different distances from one another.

16 Kendric follows the design process.
He brainstorms ideas with his parents.
He writes down the ideas and chooses the best one.
What does he do next?

Ⓐ Redesign

Ⓑ Plan and Build

Ⓒ Test and Improve

17 Chloe wants to measure the temperature.
Which tool should she use?

Ⓐ a rain gauge

Ⓑ a thermometer

Ⓒ a weather vane

18 Bo did an activity to see whether salt dissolves in water.
How could he record the results for others to see?

Ⓐ talk about his results

Ⓑ think about his results

Ⓒ draw a picture of his results

19 Look at this picture.

What moves the wagon?

Ⓐ force

Ⓑ motion

Ⓒ position

20 How are all things that make sound alike?

Ⓐ They all have strings.

Ⓑ They all vibrate to make sounds.

Ⓒ They all make sounds with a high pitch.

Name ______________________________ Date __________

Cumulative Test B

Mark one answer for each question.

1	Ⓐ	Ⓑ	Ⓒ	11	Ⓐ	Ⓑ	Ⓒ
2	Ⓐ	Ⓑ	Ⓒ	12	Ⓐ	Ⓑ	Ⓒ
3	Ⓐ	Ⓑ	Ⓒ	13	Ⓐ	Ⓑ	Ⓒ
4	Ⓐ	Ⓑ	Ⓒ	14	Ⓐ	Ⓑ	Ⓒ
5	Ⓐ	Ⓑ	Ⓒ	15	Ⓐ	Ⓑ	Ⓒ
6	Ⓐ	Ⓑ	Ⓒ	16	Ⓐ	Ⓑ	Ⓒ
7	Ⓐ	Ⓑ	Ⓒ	17	Ⓐ	Ⓑ	Ⓒ
8	Ⓐ	Ⓑ	Ⓒ	18	Ⓐ	Ⓑ	Ⓒ
9	Ⓐ	Ⓑ	Ⓒ	19	Ⓐ	Ⓑ	Ⓒ
10	Ⓐ	Ⓑ	Ⓒ	20	Ⓐ	Ⓑ	Ⓒ

❶ Look at this picture.

Which sense do you use when you put your hand on celery?

Ⓐ sight

Ⓑ taste

Ⓒ touch

❷ How do leaves help a plant?

Ⓐ Leaves hold a plant in place.

Ⓑ Leaves make food for a plant.

Ⓒ Leaves take in water from the ground.

Name ______________________________ Date __________ **End of Year**

3 What is one living thing in this environment?

Ⓐ air

Ⓑ a frog

Ⓒ rocks

4 Which is **true** about amphibians?

Ⓐ They live only on land.

Ⓑ They live only in water.

Ⓒ They live on land and in water.

❺ Which animal belongs in Group 2?

Group 1—Animals That Are Pets	Group 2—Animals That Are Wild

Ⓐ 

Ⓑ 

Ⓒ 

❻ What can plants do that animals **can not** do?

Ⓐ Plants can grow and change.

Ⓑ Plants can move to find food.

Ⓒ Plants can make their own food.

7 Anne used the design process to make this airplane.

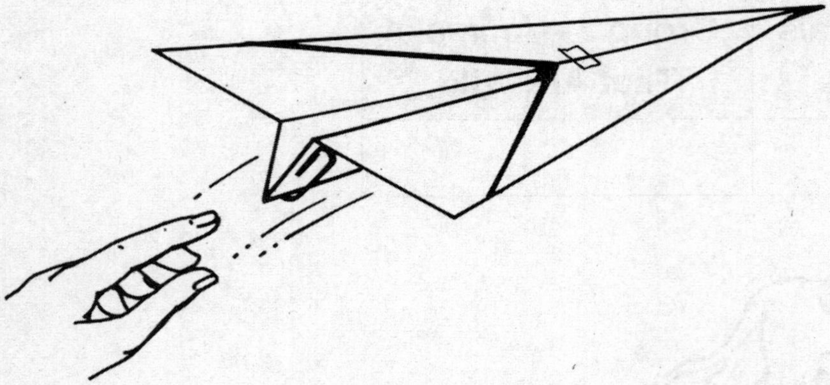

What does this picture show?

Ⓐ Communicate

Ⓑ Find a Problem

Ⓒ Test and Improve

8 What can you learn by observing a terrarium?

Ⓐ Animals do not need water to live.

Ⓑ Animals can not live in a closed environment.

Ⓒ Animals get what they need from their environment.

9 Look at these pictures.
Elsa puts a plant in a dark closet.
Luis puts a plant by a bright window.

What do you think will happen to the plants?

Ⓐ Both plants will grow much bigger.

Ⓑ The plant in the window will grow more than the plant in the closet.

Ⓒ The plant in the closet will grow more than the plant in the window.

10 What once-living thing can be found in soil?

Ⓐ rocks

Ⓑ twigs

Ⓒ water

Name ____________________ Date __________

11 Look at these pictures.
Which one shows a way people use living
things as natural resources?

Ⓐ 

Ⓑ 

Ⓒ 

12 How do you change the motion of an object?

Ⓐ by feeling it

Ⓑ by investigating it

Ⓒ by pushing or pulling it

Name ______________________________ Date __________

⓭ Look at these pictures.

Which one shows an example of water safety?

Ⓐ 

Ⓑ 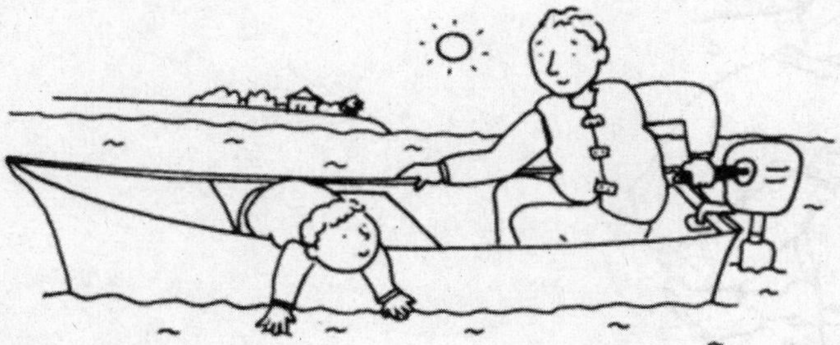

Ⓒ 

⓮ Which statement **best** tells about sound?

Ⓐ It is a kind of force.

Ⓑ It is a kind of energy.

Ⓒ It is a kind of motion.

⓯ Which season does this picture show?

Ⓐ fall

Ⓑ spring

Ⓒ winter

⓰ Why does the sun seem to move across the sky each day?

Ⓐ Earth turns each day.

Ⓑ The sun moves around Earth.

Ⓒ Shadows make it appear to move.

17 How are these stones sorted?

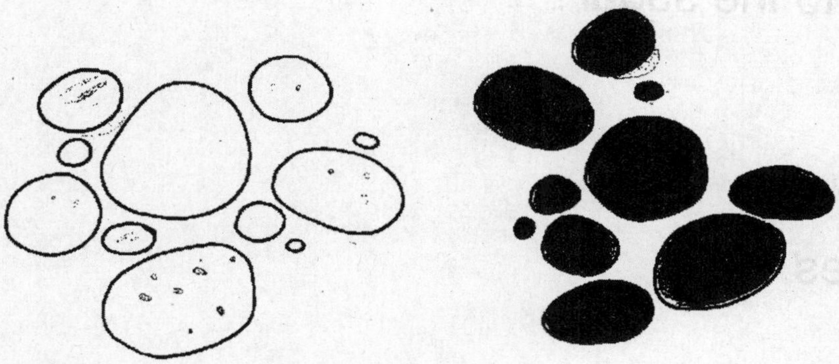

Ⓐ by color

Ⓑ by shape

Ⓒ by size

18 How could Jared make sugar dissolve **more quickly** in water?

Ⓐ He could heat the water.

Ⓑ He could add some oil to the water.

Ⓒ He could take away some of the water.

Name ______________________ Date ________

19 You make a mixture of sugar and water. What happens to the sugar?

Ⓐ It freezes.

Ⓑ It dissolves.

Ⓒ It evaporates.

20 What question does this picture answer?

Ⓐ Who wins the game?

Ⓑ How can a ball move?

Ⓒ Is the ball filled with air?

Name ______________________________ Date __________

Cumulative Test C

Mark one answer for each question.

1. Ⓐ Ⓑ Ⓒ
2. Ⓐ Ⓑ Ⓒ
3. Ⓐ Ⓑ Ⓒ
4. Ⓐ Ⓑ Ⓒ
5. Ⓐ Ⓑ Ⓒ
6. Ⓐ Ⓑ Ⓒ
7. Ⓐ Ⓑ Ⓒ
8. Ⓐ Ⓑ Ⓒ
9. Ⓐ Ⓑ Ⓒ
10. Ⓐ Ⓑ Ⓒ
11. Ⓐ Ⓑ Ⓒ
12. Ⓐ Ⓑ Ⓒ
13. Ⓐ Ⓑ Ⓒ
14. Ⓐ Ⓑ Ⓒ
15. Ⓐ Ⓑ Ⓒ
16. Ⓐ Ⓑ Ⓒ
17. Ⓐ Ⓑ Ⓒ
18. Ⓐ Ⓑ Ⓒ
19. Ⓐ Ⓑ Ⓒ
20. Ⓐ Ⓑ Ⓒ

Unit 1 How Scientists Work

Lesson 1 Quiz, p. AG 1

1. B	3. B
2. C	4. C

Lesson 2 Quiz, p. AG 2

1. A	3. A
2. C	4. C

Lesson 3 Quiz, p. AG 3

1. B	3. C
2. B	4. C

Lesson 4 Quiz, p. AG 4

1. B	3. A
2. C	4. A

Lesson 5 Quiz, p. AG 5

1. A	3. C
2. B	4. B

Unit 1 Test, pp. AG 6–10
(#1–4: 4 points each; #5–18: 5 points each)

1. B	7. B	13. C
2. C	8. C	14. C
3. B	9. A	15. B
4. A	10. C	16. A
5. B	11. C	17. A
6. B	12. B	18. A

Short Response
(6 points)

19. Sample answers:

- A ruler or tape measure measures length, height, width, and distance.
- A balance measures mass.
- A measuring cup measures an amount of liquid.
- A thermometer measures temperature.

To get full credit for this test item, children must name two tools that can be used during an investigation and describe what each tool does.

Extended Response
(8 points)

20. Sample answers:

- Use sight to look at its shape, color, and size.
- Break or bite it to hear how it sounds.
- Taste it to see how it tastes.
- Touch it to see how it feels.
- Sniff it to see how it smells.

To get full credit for this test item, children must tell four ways that they can use their senses to observe a carrot.

Unit 2 Technology All Around Us

Lesson 1 Quiz, p. AG 13

1. A	3. C
2. C	4. B

Lesson 2 Quiz, p. AG 14

1. A	3. A
2. B	4. C

Lesson 3 Quiz, p. AG 15

1. C	3. B
2. C	4. A

Lesson 4 Quiz, p. AG 16

1. C	3. B
2. A	4. B

Unit 2 Test, pp. AG 17–21
(#1–5: 4 points each; #6–18: 5 points each)

1. C	7. A	13. C
2. B	8. A	14. A
3. A	9. C	15. B
4. C	10. B	16. C
5. A	11. C	17. B
6. C	12. C	18. B

Short Response
(7 points)

19. Sample answers:
- Plan and build.
- Test and improve.

To get full credit for this test item, children must name the two steps of the design process that follow finding a problem: planning and building a design and then testing the design and finding ways to improve it.

Extended Response
(8 points)

20. Sample answers:
- Roshan will need to redesign her airplane if it does not fly across the classroom when it is tested.
- Roshan could make drawings to show what she did.

To get full credit for this test item, children must tell why the airplane might need to be redesigned and describe one way that results could be communicated.

Unit 3 Animals

Lesson 1 Quiz, p. AG 24

1. B	3. C
2. C	4. C

Lesson 2 Quiz, p. AG 25

1. C	3. B
2. A	4. B

Lesson 3 Quiz, p. AG 26

1. C	3. A
2. C	4. A

Lesson 4 Quiz, p. AG 27

1. C	3. B
2. C	4. C

Unit 3 Test, pp. AG 28–32

(#1–6: 4 points each; #7–18: 5 points each)

1. C	7. C	13. C
2. C	8. B	14. C
3. B	9. A	15. A
4. C	10. B	16. B
5. B	11. C	17. A
6. B	12. B	18. A

Short Response
(7 points)

19. Sample answers:
- They all need food and water to grow and stay healthy.
- They all need shelter and space to live and grow.
- They all need air.

To get full credit for this test item, children must name two ways that a ladybug, a baby, a lion, and a seahorse are all alike.

Extended Response
(9 points)

20. Sample answers:
- Two living things are the lizard and the cactus.
- Both need food, water, air, and space. Both grow, change, and reproduce.
- Two nonliving things are the rocks and the sun.
- Neither needs food, water, air, and space. Neither grows, changes, and reproduces.

To get full credit for this test item, children must name two living things and two nonliving things, and tell how they know that the things are living or nonliving.

Unit 4 Plants

Lesson 1 Quiz, p. AG 35

1. A	3. C
2. B	4. B

Lesson 2 Quiz, p. AG 36

1. C	3. B
2. A	4. B

Lesson 3 Quiz, p. AG 37

1. B	3. C
2. B	4. A

Lesson 4 Quiz, p. AG 38

1. B	3. C
2. B	4. C

Lesson 5 Quiz, p. AG 39

1. C	3. A
2. B	4. C

Unit 4 Test, pp. AG 40–44
(#1–5: 4 points each; #6–18: 5 points each)

1. A	7. B	13. C
2. C	8. C	14. A
3. B	9. B	15. B
4. A	10. B	16. A
5. A	11. C	17. B
6. A	12. A	18. C

Short Response
(7 points)

19. Sample answers:
- Plants get water and nutrients from the soil.
- Roots take in water and nutrients.

To get full credit for this test item, children must tell two things plants get from the soil and name the plant part that takes in these two things.

Extended Response
(8 points)

20. Sample answers:
- Trees have thick, woody stems with many branches. They can have different kinds of leaves. They have flowers or cones. They can grow very tall.
- Shrubs have many small, woody stems. Shrubs are shorter than trees and have smaller branches. They can have different kinds of leaves. They grow close to the ground.
- Grasses are small plants with soft stems. They can have different kinds of leaves. Many grasses grow flowers.

To get full credit for this test item, children must name three groups of plants and tell the characteristics that make them different from one another.

Unit 5 Environments

Lesson 1 Quiz, p. AG 47

1. C	3. B
2. B	4. A

Lesson 2 Quiz, p. AG 48

1. B	3. B
2. C	4. C

Unit 5 Test, pp. AG 49–53
(#1–13: 6 points each)

1. A	6. C	11. A
2. C	7. C	12. B
3. B	8. B	13. C
4. C	9. C	
5. A	10. A	

Short Response
(10 points)

14. Sample answers:
- The terrarium will not be a good environment.
- Living things need water. There is no water in this terrarium. The plants need sunlight. The terrarium is in a dark place with no light.

To get full credit for this test item, children must tell that the terrarium will not be a good environment for the plants and pill bugs because the terrarium does not contain things that the plants and animals need to stay alive, such as sunlight and water.

Extended Response
(12 points)

15. Sample answers:
- The arrows show the order of the food chain.
- The flower uses energy from the sun to make food.
- The rabbit eats the flower.
- The owl eats the rabbit.

To get full credit for this test item, children must tell what the arrows represent and describe the order of the food chain.

Unit 6 Earth's Resources

Lesson 1 Quiz, p. AG 56

1. C	3. C
2. B	4. A

Lesson 2 Quiz, p. AG 57

1. C	3. C
2. B	4. A

Lesson 3 Quiz, p. AG 58

1. A	3. B
2. C	4. A

Lesson 4 Quiz, p. AG 59

1. B	3. A
2. C	4. A

Lesson 5 Quiz, p. AG 60

1. A	3. B
2. B	4. C

Lesson 6 Quiz, p. AG 61

1. B	3. C
2. C	4. B

Unit 6 Test, pp. AG 62–66
(#1–5: 4 points each; #6–18: 5 points each)

1. A	7. A	13. A
2. C	8. A	14. B
3. C	9. A	15. B
4. B	10. C	16. C
5. B	11. B	17. A
6. C	12. A	18. A

Short Response
(7 points)

19. Sample answers:
- Recycling is to use old things to make new ones. You can recycle used paper to make new paper.
- Reducing is to use less of something. You can reduce by turning off lights when you leave a room.

To get full credit for this test item, children must explain the difference between recycling and reducing and give an example of each.

Extended Response
(8 points)

20. Sample answers:
- I use water to drink and bathe.
- I breathe air.
- I have grass and plants growing in soil in my yard.
- I eat cheese that is from cow's milk.

To get full credit for this test item, children must name four ways they use natural resources every day.

Unit 7 Weather and Seasons

Lesson 1 Quiz, p. AG 69

1. C	3. A
2. B	4. A

Lesson 2 Quiz, p. AG 70

1. B	3. A
2. B	4. A

Lesson 3 Quiz, p. AG 71

1. B	3. B
2. C	4. C

Unit 7 Test, pp. AG 72–76
(#1–5: 4 points each; #6–18: 5 points each)

1. C	7. A	13. A
2. B	8. C	14. A
3. B	9. B	15. B
4. B	10. A	16. B
5. C	11. C	17. C
6. A	12. C	18. A

Short Response
(7 points)
19. Sample answers:
- The third picture (the rain cloud) shows weather.
- Weather is what the air is like outside, and the third picture shows that it is raining outside.

To get full credit for this test item, children must explain that the picture of the rain cloud shows weather because it shows what the air is like outside.

Extended Response
(8 points)
20. Sample answers:
- In fall, the air gets cooler.
- In some places, leaves change color and drop off of trees.
- Some animals move to warmer places.
- People wear warmer clothes such as jackets.

To get full credit for this test item, children must tell one way that the weather changes in fall and tell one way that the seasonal change affects plants, animals, and people.

Unit 8 Objects in the Sky

Lesson 1 Quiz, p. AG 79

1. A	3. C
2. B	4. C

Lesson 2 Quiz, p. AG 80

1. C	3. C
2. B	4. A

Lesson 3 Quiz, p. AG 81

1. A	3. C
2. B	4. A

Unit 8 Test, pp. AG 82–86
(#1–6: 4 points each; #7–18: 5 points each)

1. C	7. A	13. C
2. B	8. A	14. C
3. C	9. B	15. B
4. B	10. C	16. B
5. C	11. A	17. B
6. A	12. C	18. C

Short Response
(7 points)
19. Sample answers:
- We would not see moon phases.
- The moon reflects light from the sun. With no light from the sun, the moon would be dark.

To get full credit for this test item, children must indicate that we would not see phases of the moon and must explain that the moon reflects light from the sun. The moon would be dark if there were no sun.

Extended Response
(9 points)
20. Sample answers:
- We can see the sun and moon in the day sky.
- We can see the sun only in the day sky.
- We can see many stars and the moon in the night sky.
- We can see many stars only in the night sky.

To get full credit for this test item, children must tell which faraway objects can be seen in the day sky, which faraway objects can be seen only in the day, which faraway objects can be seen in the night sky, and which faraway objects can be seen only at night.

Unit 9 All About Matter

Lesson 1 Quiz, p. AG 89

1. C
2. C
3. A
4. B

Lesson 2 Quiz, p. AG 90

1. B
2. C
3. B
4. C

Lesson 3 Quiz, p. AG 91

1. A
2. A
3. B
4. B

Lesson 4 Quiz, p. AG 92

1. B
2. A
3. C
4. A

Lesson 5 Quiz, p. AG 93

1. B
2. B
3. C
4. C

Unit 9 Test, pp. AG 94–98

(#1–7: 4 points each; #8–18: 5 points each)

1. A
2. A
3. A
4. B
5. A
6. C
7. B
8. A
9. B
10. B
11. B
12. C
13. C
14. B
15. C
16. A
17. B
18. B

Short Response

(7 points)

19. Sample answers:

- Olivia observed dissolving.
- Olivia could make this change happen faster by making the water hotter.

To get full credit for this test item, children must name the change that Olivia observed and tell how Olivia could make the change happen faster.

Extended Response

(10 points)

20. Sample answers:

- Yes, the fruit salad is a mixture.
- It is a mix of different kinds of matter.
- No, the properties of the fruit did not change.
- The parts of a mixture do not become new things.

To get full credit for this test item, children must tell whether the fruit salad is a mixture, explain their answer, tell whether the properties of the fruit salad changed, and explain that answer.

Unit 10 Forces and Energy

Lesson 1 Quiz, p. AG 101

1. C
2. B
3. B
4. C

Lesson 2 Quiz, p. AG 102

1. C
2. A
3. C
4. A

Lesson 3 Quiz, p. AG 103

1. B
2. B
3. C
4. C

Lesson 4 Quiz, p. AG 104

1. B
2. C
3. A
4. A

Lesson 5 Quiz, p. AG 105

1. C
2. A
3. C
4. A

Unit 10 Test, pp. AG 106–110

(#1–5: 4 points each; #6–18: 5 points each)

1. B
2. A
3. C
4. A
5. A
6. A
7. A
8. C
9. C
10. A
11. B
12. C
13. A
14. B
15. B
16. C
17. C
18. B

Short Response
(7 points)

19. Sample answers:
- Force can change the cart's speed.
- Force can change the cart's direction.

To get full credit for this test item, children must tell two ways that pushing a cart changes the cart's motion.

Extended Response
(8 points)

20. Sample answers:
- in a straight line: a child going straight down a slide
- back and forth: a swing
- in a zigzag: a car on a zigzag road
- round and round: a merry-go-round

To get full credit for this test item, children must name four ways objects can move and name something that moves each of these four ways.

Cumulative Test A, pp. AG 113–122
(5 points each)

1. C	8. A	15. B
2. A	9. B	16. A
3. A	10. C	17. A
4. A	11. B	18. B
5. C	12. A	19. A
6. B	13. C	20. B
7. A	14. B	

Cumulative Test B, pp. AG 124–133
(5 points each)

1. C	8. C	15. C
2. B	9. B	16. B
3. A	10. C	17. B
4. B	11. A	18. C
5. A	12. A	19. A
6. C	13. B	20. B
7. A	14. A	

Cumulative Test C, pp. AG 135–144
(5 points each)

1. C	8. C	15. C
2. B	9. B	16. A
3. B	10. B	17. A
4. C	11. C	18. A
5. A	12. C	19. B
6. C	13. C	20. B
7. C	14. B	